About the author

Emanuele Trevi is an Italian w_
has written many critical essays on poets and writers, and
his book on the poet Pietro Tripodo won the Sandro Onofri
Prize. He was creative director of the publisher Fazi, and,
with Marco Lodoli, he edited a school anthology. Trevi has
served on the jury for several literary awards and has written
for magazines and various national newspapers, including
La Repubblica, La Stampa, and *il manifesto.* In 2012, he won
the European Literature Prize for his book *Something Written.* It was a finalist for Italy's most prestigious literary prize,
the Strega Prize, and was on the Italian bestseller lists for
many months. His work has been translated into over ten
languages.

About the translator

Ann Goldstein is an editor at *The New Yorker.* She has translated works by, among others, Elena Ferrante, Pier Paolo
Pasolini, and Alessandro Baricco, and is the editor of the
Complete Works of Primo Levi in English. She has been the
recipient of a Guggenheim fellowship, the PEN Renato Pog-
gioli prize, and awards from the Italian Ministry of Foreign
Affairs and the American Academy of Arts and Letters.

Something Written

Emanuele Trevi

Something Written

Translated from the Italian
by Ann Goldstein

World Editions

Published in Great Britain in 2016 by World Editions Ltd., London

www.worldeditions.org

First published as *Qualcosa di scritto* in Italy in 2012 by Ponte alle Grazie,
an imprint of Adriano Salani Editore S.p.A.

British Library Cataloguing-in-Publication Data
A catalogue record for this book is available on request
from the British Library

ISBN 978-94-6238-080-6

Typeset in Minion Pro

This project has been funded with support from the European Commission.
This publication reflects the views only of the author, and the Commission
cannot be held responsible for any use which may be made of the
information contained herein.

Co-funded by the
Creative Europe Programme
of the European Union

This book has been translated thanks to a translation grant awarded by
the Italian Ministry for Foreign Affairs
Questo libro e' stato tradotto grazie ad un contributo alla traduzione
assegnato dal Ministero degli Affari Esteri Italiano

Distribution Europe (except the Netherlands and Belgium):
Turnaround Publisher Services, London
Distribution the Netherlands and Belgium: CB, Culemborg,
the Netherlands

Something Written

for my father

It's a novel, but it's not written the way real novels are written: its language is that of essays, of newspaper articles, of reviews, of private letters, even of poetry.

PIER PAOLO PASOLINI, *Petrolio*
(letter to Alberto Moravia)

For this was why my work was often insufficiently illuminated; the voltage was there, but by restricting myself to the techniques of whatever form I was working in, I was not using everything I knew about writing—all I'd learned from film scripts, plays, reportage, poetry, the short story, novellas, the novel. A writer ought to have all his colors, all his abilities available on the same palette for mingling (and, in suitable instances, simultaneous application). But how?

TRUMAN CAPOTE, *Music for Chameleons*

Among the many—too many—people who worked for Laura Betti at the Pier Paolo Pasolini Foundation in Rome, all of them endowed with a colorful store of more or less unpleasant memories, I believe that I can boast of, if nothing else, above-average endurance. Not that I was at all spared the extravagant daily persecution that the Madwoman (as I soon took to calling her, in my own mind) felt it her duty to inflict on her subordinates. On the contrary, I was so irredeemably *odious* to her (there is no more precise word) that I succeeded in plucking all the strings of her protean sadism: from the ceaseless invention of humiliating nicknames to real physical threat. Every time I entered the offices of the foundation, in a dark, massive corner building on Piazza Cavour, not far from Castel Sant'Angelo, I sensed almost physically the animal hostility, the uncontrollable rage that flashed, like the zigzag lightning in a comic book, from behind the lenses of her big square sunglasses. The standard greetings immediately followed. 'Good morning, little slut, did you finally figure out that it's time to GIVE HIM YOUR ASS? Or do you think you can still get away with it?!? But you don't fool ME, you sweet-talking little slut, it takes a lot more than someone like you'—and this first blast of amenities was ended only by the eruption of a laugh that seemed to come from a subterranean cavern, and was made more threatening by the counterpoint of an indescribable sound halfway between a roar and a sob. Very rarely could the avalanche of insults dumped on the unfortunate victim be traced back to meaningful concepts. Besides, as a general rule, the Madwoman detested meaning, in every form. There was no human instrument that in her hands did not become a dangerously explosive device. And language was no exception. Her tirades revolved on the pivot of an offensive epithet, savored with pleasure and constantly repeated, as if the gist of the conversation resided there, in the pure formulation of the insult. If addressed to a male, the epithet was generally feminine. Even people she liked, and admired, had to put up with this sort of symbolic emasculation. Alberto Moravia, for example, to whom she was very attached, at a certain point became 'grandma,' and there was nothing to be done about it.[1] The entire remainder of the conversation, once the insult had been uttered, was pure and simple improvisation—a Piranesian prison of malevolence and contempt, heedless of logic and syntax. 'Little slut'—that was from the start the essence, the perfect expression of what I inspired in her. Sweet-talking, vain, lying, *fascist* little slut. Jesuit, murderer. Ambitious. As for me, though I wasn't yet thirty, I had already, like the prisoner of Edgar Allan Poe, groped my way around the walls of my character, which, as in all dungeons, were properly damp and dark. That the Madwoman was not completely wrong I could easily enough admit. What really infuriated her was my wish to please her, my ostentatious lack of aggressiveness, and, ultimately, the indifference that has always been my sole defense against the threats of the world.

There was no doubt about the type of damned who would willingly take charge of tormenting for eternity that sort of Dantesque monster, enveloped in the smoke of the cigarettes she left burning in the ashtray, with her excessive bulk and her hair, of a terrifying reddish-orange hue, knotted in a tuft that inevitably made you think, when she shook it, of the jet of a whale, or the crest of a psychotic pineapple. Laura hated hypocrites and, more generally, all those persons who, incapable of expressing themselves, appeared to her as *fake*, condemned to hide behind a papier-mâché mask. This was what I liked about her, even as I suffered the consequences. It seemed to me that, hidden in the recesses of all that hostility, there was a kind of medicine, a lesson leading to salvation. And so, from the moment I started going to the foundation, where I quickly gained experience of every sort of temperamental storm, from the slightest to the most severe, I had concluded that the time I spent there, in the shadow of that mental Chernobyl, was time well spent. What was it, exactly—a punishment that I had inflicted on myself by myself to expiate some grave sin? A spiritual exercise imbued with the most rigorous masochism? At a certain point, there could be no doubt, the Madwoman would fire me, as she had dozens of others (some such relationships had lasted no more than a few hours). But I, as far as it was in my power, would do nothing to leave. My job, which wasn't very complicated, consisted of tracking down all the interviews that Pasolini had done: from the first, which went back to the time of *Street Kids*, up to the most famous, the one he did with Furio Colombo a few hours before his death.[2] Once the material was gathered, I would assemble it into a book. Nothing exceptional, apart from the labor of doing it; and Laura was very generous when it came to money. She liked to tear off checks, after writing them in her dramatic way, transforming every compensation into an undeserved gift, something stolen from her greatness of soul, and a clear, unalterable confirmation of that greatness. If she could, she would have carved those checks in marble. She was also very skillful at getting hold of any type of public financing, to support all the initiatives of the foundation, and to pay a few regular employees: a great archivist, Giuseppe Iafrate, who was as patient and detached as a Tibetan bonze, and a couple of girls whom she flayed alive but who, without admitting it to themselves, ended up almost loving her. As far as I was concerned, inevitably, sooner or later, I would be fired: I was mathematically certain of it. The fact is that Laura had her own notions about how to publish those interviews. They were crazy, incomprehensible ideas, of no practical use, and she tortured me about them for hours. 'Listen to me, little slut, these interviews of Pier Paolo are BURNING, do you understand? You've read them. Even you must get it. *Burn-ing*. And so, in this book, all the words have to FLY, you understand what *a form that flies* is? You have to make them fly, fly, fly.' And I: Yes, Laura, I absolutely agree, that's what I want, too, to make them *fly*. Like eagles. In reality, I wanted to publish those interviews as they deserved, and I would never ever understand how they would be made to fly. I continued on the only path that I considered possible. The accomplished fact—I predicted—would trigger the catastrophe. And that was how it happened. In the meantime, having tracked down all the interviews, I had arranged them in chronological order, taking care to eliminate the mistakes and misprints of the newspapers, translating some from French or English, and preparing lengthy, informative notes. Finally, I had written an introductory essay, in which I tried to explain how Pasolini, more than any other artist of his time, had considered the interview a literary genre that was anything but minor and casual. At that point, I could no longer put off the reckoning. For the entire duration of my last meeting with Laura, in her office, the sharp blade of a box cutter quivered a few millimeters from my jugular. The chain of insults reached levels of verbal tightrope-walking worthy of a Rabelais. I understood how precise and literal the expression 'foaming with rage' is. I was afraid at any moment of bringing on a stroke, for which I would have been in some way responsible. The wretched file containing all my work ended up, not without the usual melodramatic solemnity, in the wastebasket. The threat of that blade made an impression, but I didn't think the Madwoman would go so far as to kill or wound me—it wasn't that type of madness. Apart from the assault of cold steel, I had foreseen it all, in my insistence on carrying out the work as I thought best. Many months had passed, more than a year, in fact, since I started going to the foundation. I worked slowly, and other duties had been added, which delayed the collection and preparation of those damn interviews. What ended so abruptly had been, therefore, a period of time that was in all senses very *instructive*—I don't know how else to describe it—for me. I consider it a kind of apprenticeship. We all need to learn something, and, before that, learn to learn. But the only schools that are truly worth attending are the ones we don't choose, those whose thresholds we cross, so to speak, by chance; just as the only materials that we ought to study deeply are those which don't have a precise name, and still less a rational method of being studied. Everything else, finally, is relative. Laura was a raucous and unpleasant textbook to page through, but full of revelations that, if they remained hard to describe, were no less penetrating. And to this I would immediately add, because it's a fundamental fact, the publication of *Petrolio*, which struck Laura's little kingdom in Piazza Cavour like a thunderbolt, like a handful of gunpowder on a crackling fire.

Petrolio is a large fragment, what remains of a mad, visionary work, outside the rules, revelatory. Pasolini works on it from the spring of 1972 up until the days immediately preceding his death, the night between the first and second of November, 1975. *Petrolio* is a savage beast. It's an account of a process of knowledge and transformation. It's a becoming aware of the world and an experiment on itself. Technically: an initiation. *Petrolio* is published by Einaudi in 1992, seventeen years after P.P.P.'s death, in the series Supercoralli. It has a white cover, and the letters of the author's name and the title are red and black—it's an object of rare beauty. This posthumous publication has two editors: Maria Careri and Graziella Chiarcossi. The long note at the end of the volume is by the great philologist Aurelio Roncaglia, a longtime friend of Pasolini. One can read *Petrolio* as a provocation, as a confession, as an exploration. And, obviously, as a will. All blood-stained. It should immediately be added that in 1992, when *Petrolio* is torn from the blessed sleep of the unpublished, such books are no longer being written. They are creations that have become incomprehensible to the overwhelming majority of the world. Something happened. Compared with the literature of 1975, the literature of 1992 seems much more—how to put it?—*impoverished*. The diversity of genres, and the entire, infinite range of nuances, impurities, individual variations, seems to have almost disappeared, reduced to a single requirement, a single preoccupation: telling stories, writing a good novel. In a few years, in other words, a mutation has taken place that is so radical and so irreversible that *Petrolio*, emerging from the bottom of the drawer, seems to come not from another epoch but from another dimension, like one of those objects made of an unknown material, resistant to the laws of physics and Euclidean geometry, which in science-fiction stories break into our world from some recess or hole in space-time. But what happened that is so serious? For more than two hundred years (since the times of Diderot, of Sterne, just to establish a point) literature didn't stop, one might say, running. It pursued an ideal end, always a little beyond the possibility of the individual. From its own wastes and failures it extracted valuable fuels. Among human fields of knowledge, it could be considered a cutting edge. More destiny than profession, its practice produced for every generation forms of holiness and folly fated to remain exemplary for a long time. What the Christian martyrs, the ascetics, the great sinners enlightened by Grace represented in medieval legends was now embodied by equally exceptional individuals like Mandelstam, Céline, Sylvia Plath, Mishima. Thomas Bernhard hoped that his neighbors would use him to frighten the children: 'If you don't behave, Mr. Bernhard will come and take you away!!!' Today, on the contrary, the greatest aspiration of writers is to be *loved* by parents and children, like Santa Claus (women writers, obviously, will aspire to resemble the Befana—but the vocation of *bearer of gifts* is the same). Taking into account innumerable failures, that now faded conception of literary writing continued to proceed on the stilts of Experiment and the Unprecedented. A natural elective affinity made it the accomplice of every sort of revolt and subversion, whether the target was the political order or the habits of inner life. All this we call, using a word that is somewhat worn but, all in all, adequate, 'modernity.' Almost automatically connected to the word is the idea, identical in its infinite variety of styles and individual visions, that literature is an irreplaceable form of knowledge of the world. Not a storehouse of good plots for movies, much less a product intended for an illusory 'spiritual' elevation, but a challenge, an irreparable outrage, the final blow intended to drive the nail into the very heart of truth. Born in 1922, Pier Paolo Pasolini never even had to ponder these concepts, which today sound so exotic, archeological. Being modern was his primordial soup, the state of departure, a conditioned reflex. Like many men of his generation, he couldn't have suspected what the future held—if he had remained alive, he would only have had to take note of it, like many others. Until the end, in short, P.P.P. worked as a perfect representative of the modern age, not knowing that he was one of the last. The years of *Petrolio* are the same as those of Pynchon's *Gravity's Rainbow*, for one example, or of the *Anti-Oedipus* of Deleuze and Guattari, for another. There's nothing, in these vast and ambitious works, that lets us suspect the least awareness of being, in some way, the end of the match. As long as it lasted, modernity convinced everyone that it was eternal. Each generation raised the bar, like a high jumper who is testing himself, and found a way of getting over it. Then, suddenly, just in the period when the pile of pages of *Petrolio* is waiting in the shadows for its moment, that prodigious machine comes to a halt—perhaps forever. Not that literature 'dies,' as for more than a century people hoped or feared (or both together). It remains—alas—more alive and well than ever: if anything, it drastically reduces, once and for all, its potentialities and its prerogatives. This reduction should necessarily and in every case be understood as a decline. The fact is that by the mid-eighties the most important writer of the epoch is surely Raymond Carver. An artist who is anything but modest, and the author of unforgettable stories like *Cathedral*, Carver perfectly exemplifies the extraordinary change that had taken place. In his books, we are present at the disconcerting spectacle of a literature that *no longer thinks*. The writer's sole task is that of the *storyteller*. The only world he talks about is the one that he knows empirically—the portion of the cage that has been allotted to him. His only hope is that a good number of readers like his stories. It's no coincidence, naturally, that, more than any other literary or human influence, Carver endured that of his editor, the notorious Gordon Lish. Lish, a handsome man with the sharp features of a bird of prey, is the founder of a new type of technocrat of writing—technocrats who, scattered throughout the four corners of the world, are obsessed by efficacy, by *functioning*, as the supreme duty of the literary product. The comparison (made possible by more recent editions) between what Carver wrote out of his own head and what Lish made of it is one of the most terrifying and instructive testimonies offered by literary history. It would be superficial to claim that the editor makes the material he works on 'salable.' That can happen, but not everything the editor lays his hands on becomes gold. His secret vocation is incomparably more metaphysical, more fiendish than any innocent commercial desire. What the editor intends to do is *to transform all of literature entirely into narrative*. Forgive me this insistent recourse to the historical present. But it seems to me the most fitting style in which to render a phenomenon as ineluctable as it is sudden, similar to a spiritual coup d'état. And so: an era begins in which literary excellence increasingly coincides with the ability to entertain. The writer: he who, watched over by his editor, the most important human presence in his life, invents plots. This means that the fundamental emotion he seeks to rouse in the reader is *recognition*. How true, how all this resembles me! It's really like that! But in order for this delicate and uncertain psychological miracle to really take place, the writer has to pay dues. At the cost of sacrificing remarkable aspects of his life and his character, he has to *resemble his readers as closely as possible*. To be made, as they say, of the same clay. Mutual support, and mutual corruption (only like corrupts like). The editor: he who without respite strives to make the writer and his reader *homogeneous*. And here, precisely defined, is the Copernican revolution that in 1992 makes that monster from the past that is *Petrolio* practically illegible. The assumption of Pasolini's writing—one might almost say his basic method—is exactly the fact that he, P.P.P., doesn't resemble anyone. Not even History, that infallible plane, smoothed out the anomaly that he is. To enable a reader to *recognize* in his pages something of himself and the existence that surrounds him—that doesn't even occur to P.P.P. It would be equivalent, for him, to a failure. Already in his own time, Pasolini thought of himself as a survivor, an isolate, a force of the past. But if he had come back to life in 1992 along with the manuscript of *Petrolio*, he would truly have been identical to the resurrected man Dante speaks of in the *Convivio*, who no longer understands the language spoken in his city.

Luckily, these big collective changes leave madmen, desperate cases, untouched—all those who can't make it. Laura Betti and *Petrolio*: one of those careless chemical reactions that in cartoons end with a deafening boom and the laboratory in ruins. For the aspiring writer I was at the time, this was a subject for reflection. Because literature, understood as a grand experiment on the limitations of the human, should *always* be this: a detonator, a disaster that produces irreversible changes in life. A factor for *imbalance*. The more genuine greatness a book possesses, the more capable it should be of fertilizing forms of madness adequate to that greatness. But this is very rare, and not exactly official. The critics, the professors, the *intellectuals* arrive, cold and serious, like the black rabbits at Pinocchio's bedside. Tenacious and patient, mediocrity always asserts its rights. If you're looking for a mastermind in the death of P.P.P., mediocrity should be first on the list of suspects. Homicide, incidentally, is an anything but marginal number in its repertory. What I mean to declare, with the good faith of the witness, is that Laura Betti was the ideal reader of *Petrolio*. What does that expression mean, ideal reader? Laura was firmly, unshakably, convinced that she was the only person in the world who understood P.P.P.—the man and his multifaceted work. What was in effect the content of that understanding we cannot know. Certain secrets only she knew. Maybe the wicked were plotting in the shadows, impeding or delaying their revelation. You had to hint, to proceed obliquely, to let out only half of certain remarks, as if the silent half contained some unspeakable truths. Laura knew perfectly all the intonations and nuances of the jargon of plotters. If she had only wanted to, she would have been an extraordinary paranoiac. But paranoia was only one of the colors on her palette, one possibility among others, a form of madness too small for her aspirations. Despite the atmosphere of a modest, dusty archive, relatively pre-technology, the rooms of the Pasolini Foundation on Piazza Cavour were the avant-garde of a cruel and silent war. The stolid, reassuring normality of life, in that chaotic, heavily trafficked place in Rome, was only an appearance, yet another mask put on by an unfathomable reality, imbued with Violence and Secrecy. The enormous bulk of the Palace of Justice, with its garish and threatening shapes, loomed over the piazza; Orson Welles had used it as a set for some scenes of his film inspired by Kafka's *The Trial*. The architect of the wretched Palace, Guglielmo Calderini, was accused of building that immense structure on treacherous terrain, on sand and clay, exposed to infiltrations from the Tiber. It seems that the polemics were so bitter he was driven to suicide. But I don't want to lose sight of Laura. It can't be denied that the idea of being the privileged addressee, and in some way the heir and guardian of a work, is an obvious sign of madness—how else to define it? At the same time, we can't rule out that a certain amount of madness is an essential element the moment we decide that something is truly important, even *crucial* for us. Words that seem addressed to all our kind (as by definition the words of a writer are) become charged with an unbearable degree of intentionality. Where the collective appears hypocritical and lacking in attention, the individual can go so far as to see himself as the unique recipient of a message, a will, a mandate. All of which, it must be admitted, can make a literary text extraordinarily effective, capable of generating decisive inner repercussions. Literature's only chance of lasting and of having an effect is entrusted not to collective judgments and values but to individual human beings, to their capacity to admit that they are alone and unique, to the unnamable drives and unconfessable hopes that determine their fate. Gradually, as the file of articles on *Petrolio* expanded, Laura's rage found new, inexhaustible nourishment. In her typical day, the morning reading of the newspapers represented a kind of general trial, in view of more demanding exercises of madness. Like practicing scales for a pianist. She brimmed with contempt and pity as she waved around those poor crackling sheets of paper. She oozed the blackest sarcasm. The clippings that accumulated in a fat cardboard folder were the concrete proof, and the eloquent symbol, of the pettiness and the cowardice of humanity. Was she wrong? The portraits she offered me of the most illustrious pens of Italian criticism and literature can't be reported. 'Those little men ... all fags of the worst kind ... the *Catholic kind* ... are not worthy of even mentioning the name of Pier Paolo ... HAHAHAHAHAHAHA [*sob*] ... secret fags, with their little wifey ... their career as spongers ... you understood me, SPONGERS, people good for nothing but swiping something!!! Like Wimpy, Popeye's friend: as soon as THE MEATBALLS are ready, they show up. And you, little slut, with your polite manners, you're getting ready to join that fine crowd ... but why not just kill yourself?' And indeed: why not kill myself, just in time, before I turned into one of those shits, those spongers? The day comes when the idea of being the maker of one's own destiny is revealed as an illusion. One begins to feel like a billiard ball on an inclined plane, incapable of braking or changing direction. The Madwoman's laugh thundered in my head, like the indecipherable warning of an obese Fury, while I rolled faster and faster toward everything that fate had in store for me.

Encounters that truly, as they say, *leave a mark* are extremely rare. I mean an indelible mark—more a scar or even an amputation than a system of memories. The majority of the people we meet, sad to say, do not cause in us a profound reaction, much less an even minimal change. We would be perfectly the same without ever having met them. But that depressing rule only makes the exception more dangerous. There are always individuals who play in the life of their fellows a role that I wouldn't know how to describe better than *disastrous*. Reflecting on Laura's devotion to P.P.P. while witnessing all its disconcerting and turbulent manifestations, I often happened to think of him, of P.P.P., the way one might consider a hurricane by contemplating the uprooted trees, the blown-off roofs, the collapsed embankments it leaves behind. Indirect knowledge (of one person through another) is undeniably a source of all sorts of errors, but it can stimulate the muscle of intuition. Was P.P.P. the *cause* of the stunning and noisy *effect* that I was facing? As Cioran says, inner violence is contagious. That means that exceptional individuals, engaged in complex and laborious—not to say dangerous—experiments on themselves, end up, without taking responsibility for it, dragging into their treacherous current those who are near them.[3] Yet the saddest part is that these individuals not only have no direct responsibility for the havoc they bring to others' lives but most of the time *don't even realize what they've done.* They don't have the time; they have to proceed straight on their path—wherever it's taking them. Probably, they believe in good faith that their intimates are endowed with a character fairly similar to theirs, and so are capable of watching out for themselves, without harboring harmful dependencies. The Cause ignores the Effect—isn't all the sadness, injustice, irremediable *dissymmetry* of life concealed in this little formula, savoring of philosophy? It should be added that P.P.P. died so suddenly and mysteriously, not to say atrociously, that he was inevitably transformed into a kind of Hamlet-like ghost: still more present, requiring still more attention than alive, if that was possible. Like everything that has to do with common sense and with the shrewd management of life, the so-called elaboration of mourning is not a very romantic or poetic idea. It implies the need to keep going, attributing to time the virtue of a palliative drug. He who dies lies down—says the adage, irrefutably—and he who lives resigns himself. It was this prosaic but necessary going on that Laura's life seemed to lack. Rather than proceeding, it rolled, spun around the unmoving pivot of something that, although absent, was more present than any presence. Being around her, you inevitably ended up perceiving its presence. Livid and mutilated by beatings, unburied and stinking, the corpse of P.P.P. hovered in the rooms of the foundation like a sinister and indecipherable warning. What do the dead want from us?

When Laura's bursts of rage became uncontrollable, I beat a retreat from the foundation, as discreetly as possible, and wandered around the neighborhood of Piazza Cavour, waiting until she cooled down or had something to do elsewhere. Aimless wandering has always been a specialty of mine. It creates the illusion that life is long, that there's time for everything. As everyone in Rome knows, in any neighborhood and at any hour of the day or night, there are more people lounging around with no purpose than those engaged in some concrete business. Thus one morning, as I was ambling along the Lungotevere after having slipped out of the clutches of the Madwoman, I happened on the Museum of the Souls in Purgatory. A visit in all senses illuminating. The museum, whose holdings are contained in a single, small bare room, is in the church of the Sacro Cuore del Suffragio, a questionable imitation in reinforced concrete of the Duomo of Milan, almost at the corner of Via Ulpiano. In 1897, inside the just finished fake-Gothic church, a fire broke out, and in a smoke stain left by the flames on one wall the priest recognized, unmistakably, the features of a suffering face. For that priest, whose name was Vittore Jouet, it was like receiving a command directly from on High: and he began to travel around Europe, in search of every type of object that showed evidence of contact between the living and the dead—the sufferers in Purgatory who asked for Masses for the repose of their souls and charitable works to alleviate and shorten their punishments. Astonishing Catholic bookkeeping: one of the most remarkable manifestations of human perversion and candor. Almost all the exhibits displayed in the cases of the Museum of the Souls in Purgatory are objects of daily use: books, pillowcases, items of clothing, humble tools for work. On these objects appear signs of burning, often in the form of the fingers of a hand. In his adventurous research Father Jouet followed a sort of theory, a general criterion: death is manifested by a burning pressure; it leaves an indelible trace of its passage, of its summons. This is the most terrifying and direct of languages—*contact*. All those dead, besides, are basically reprimanding the living. They are rousing them from forgetfulness and recalling them to inescapable duties of piety. Put crudely: they're breaking their balls. Because life, like all special states, needs to guarantee its own ephemeral duration through egoism, and a certain degree of unconsciousness. Affinities between places have always struck me much more than affinities between human beings, which are after all inevitable. And undoubtedly the Museum of the Souls in Purgatory and the Pasolini Foundation, a few dozen meters apart, were so similar that they could be considered two parts, or variations, or branches, *of the same place*. But at this point I have to implore the patient reader not to attribute to me, jumping ahead, a banal and false thought. I don't in the least intend to transform the ghost of P.P.P. into a vapid, literary-page metaphor, declaring that that ghost exercises, or has exercised, some form of influence on Italian 'culture' or 'society.' Among other things, 'culture' and 'society' lie totally outside my interests; their nature as essentially hypocritical conventions makes me suspect that in fact they don't really interest *anyone*—much less those who, for lack of something better, boast about them. Father Jouet, the inventor of the Museum of the Souls in Purgatory, would never have been so delirious as to declare that his ghosts were capable of frightening and admonishing the Church, or the community of Catholics. It doesn't work like that. The action of ghosts is effective when it's addressed to the individual, to his weakness and his solitude. And, as the books and the scorched clothing preserved in the museum's dusty cases were displayed as obvious proofs of supernatural contact, so Laura's mind, equally burned and blackened, seemed to me the tangible sign of a presence, of a request so urgent and desperate as to eliminate the border between life and death.

Something written. Neither more nor less—this is the formula that on various occasions surfaces in *Petrolio* as the most fitting definition of the work that is taking shape. The most fitting definition, in fact, of the nature of a text that, like a shadow or a sticky secretion, can't, or is unwilling to, detach itself completely from its origin: a human being, a living body ('I *live*,' Pasolini states, not coincidentally, on one of the first pages, 'the genesis of my book.' But that this is a genesis is not a simple premise: this particular God, by vocation or necessity, does not unglue himself from his Creation, he stays there, creating it, he can't help it, no seventh day is provided for him).[4] According to the circumstances, *something written*, that shapeless monster (all true monsters are shapeless and all truly shapeless things are monstrous), might resemble a novel, an essay, a mythological poem, a travel book, a collection of linked stories like *The Thousand and One Nights* or *The Canterbury Tales*. But no genre of writing, considered in the abstract, not even a diary, could support the weight of that presence, of that breath that fogs every mirror: him, P.P.P., in flesh and blood. 'I have spoken to the reader as myself,' he confesses in a letter to his friend Alberto Moravia, an old fox who instantly grasps the gravity and the enormity of the sin. I was no longer able, P.P.P.

explains, to take on with humility the garments of 'a narrator.' In the end, and in spite of all appearances, a narrator is 'like all other narrators.' More precisely, it's a convention. Not him: he has no wish to play that game, which, since the world began, is the game of literature, which in turn imitates the Game of Creation. *Something written*: it means to maintain through words the same painful intimacy that connects the child who pees in his bed to the warm stain spreading on the sheet. And at the same time, without contradiction, with that shame completely expiated, *something written* means to exercise over the body of the language a pressure that is not only mental, not only cultural. To begin to live a form is like saying that starting from there, from that pressure which produces a kind of mold, an individual begins to take possession of reality. In a way that, Pasolini observes, can only be violent and brutal, as happens in every act of possession. And it's not only the act that is completed by the writing of the book, the search for the 'sense of reality' in order to possess it, which can't happen without violence and brutality. It's also a self-destruction. 'I wished,' Pasolini says plainly, '*also* to free myself from myself, that is to die.' To live his own creation to the end of life: as when one dies in childbirth. But the comparison with childbirth isn't completely adequate, and immediately afterward he suggests a second, which is even more apt: '*as in effect one dies, ejaculating into the mother's womb.*'

Personally, I hate it when it's said of Pasolini that he was 'uncomfortable,' as if he were a sofa, or 'prophetic,' as if he were some kind of circus huckster. The intellectual glory that derives from so-called prophecies, among other things, has always been very dubious, if not suspect. At exactly fifty, when he starts work on *Petrolio*, between the spring and summer of 1972, writing down in 'less than an hour' a schematic plot, Pasolini has a lot to do besides peer into the darkness of the future. What we read is, if anything, the story of *an initiation*. The allusions to techniques and rituals of initiation are so frequent and precise in *Petrolio* (even from the point of view of the vocabulary) as to leave no room for doubt. Considered as a method of gaining knowledge of reality, initiation has nothing to do with the usual rational procedures. It's a leap forward, a traumatic break in continuity. It implies a radical and irreversible metamorphosis and tends, in its ultimate stage, toward a vision rather than toward knowledge that is translatable into abstract terms, as a political, or literary, or philosophical ideology would be. At the height of the vision, the one who knows can no longer be distinguished from what is known, the internal from the external, desire from its object. In a supreme, ecstatic flash of awareness, it finally becomes clear that, concealed in the infinite number of stories that can be told, there is always *a single story*. That infinity is an illusion, from which we can awaken. The man who sprayed his seed into the 'maternal womb,' as P.P.P. calls it, does not turn back. That same Oedipal image of the maternal womb has the air of a premise, which leads to a further image, even richer in meaning. A motif that returns often in *Petrolio* is the earth. Isn't the earth the 'maternal womb' of every living thing? But in *Petrolio* the metaphor isn't at all generic. If anything, a particular type of earth is evoked: poor, clayey, polluted by all kinds of trash, sprouting stunted, sparse blades of grass. It's the land of the big open spaces of the Roman periphery, surrounded on its edges by the outline of the new developments and the old neighborhoods. Mother earth and no man's earth. The anonymity of these portions of reality makes them all perfectly identical, interchangeable. They vibrate in unison, like unnamable energy fields protected by their very insignificance. It's also true that in P.P.P.'s story *one* of those places, in particular, played the role of last stop and scene of the crime. It's the 'vile suburban moorland covered with foul garbage,' as Gianfranco Contini calls it in his unforgettable *Testimonianza per Pier Paolo Pasolini* (Testimony for Pier Paolo Pasolini*).

I had been working at the foundation for a few weeks when Laura organized a kind of public pilgrimage to the Idroscalo of Ostia, including members of the local council, writers, journalists, some old friends of P.P.P. One has to acknowledge that the Madwoman had a distinct talent for organization. She loved the telephone and lists of people to call. Depending on who was at the other end of the line, she conversed, flattered, erupted in terrible threats and in celebrated streams of insults. She slammed down the receiver cursing to herself and, right away, the preceding having been checked off on the list, started with another number. She considered a busy signal a personal affront, to be made up for on the spot by resorting to the urgent-call warning. If the world was shamefully forgetting P.P.P., she made sure, engagement book in hand, to fling him back in its face of shit. The purpose of the raid on the Idroscalo, if I remember correctly, was to expose the state of total abandon of the place, which at the time was in fact a kind of open dump, littered with rusty scrap iron, condoms, rotting mattresses, syringes left by addicts, piles of bricks and other waste materials from construction sites. In the middle of that dense, tangled growth towered the shapeless mass of what was supposed to have been a monument. Vandalism and weather, which often come together to produce remarkable examples of involuntary beauty, the most sublime of beauties, had transformed that work of abstract style, in itself extremely banal, into an eloquent symbol of transience and desperation. From the cracked and crumbling gray concrete the iron bars of the frame emerged, like the skeleton of a carcass devoured by a herd of predators. No plaque, no inscription explained the origin and the purpose of that disturbing ruin. Today, that no man's land abandoned to itself and its grim memories is part of a protected area, entrusted to the Law for the Protection of Birds. The author of *The Hawks and the Sparrows* might perhaps have appreciated the ironic coincidence. The monument has been restored, there are pathways and benches. A marble plaque bears the famous opening lines of *The Cry of the Excavator*. Only love, only knowledge counts, et cetera, et cetera. One might have chosen something more original, but no need to overdo the snobbishness. In other words, a decorous insignificance has ended up triumphing over the old scene of the crime. And from my point of view the cleanup has removed, along with the dirt and the squalor (which are not always and not necessarily entirely negative), the indefinable but precious sense of authenticity that hovered over the place, along with clouds of an intolerable anguish. Can we imagine a State so far-seeing, so *philosophical*, that it would have the courage to honor the memory of a poet, of a man as genuine and courageous as P.P.P., with an illegal garbage dump? A people capable of understanding the subtle pedagogy of such a monument would perhaps no longer even need a State. In any case, leaving aside further reflections that might appear futile, I return in memory to the small crowd (maybe forty people) that, enlisted by Laura, had gathered at the edge of the garden in the center of Piazza Cavour, waiting to leave for the Idroscalo. The caravan was headed by a blue city car, belonging to Gianni Borgna, who at the time was a councilor in charge of culture and had for many years been calling for a dispassionate re-examination of all the evidence of the crime and for a reopening of the official investigation and the judicial case. It's toward that car that Laura heads, arranging her mass on the back seat with the usual breathless theatricality and enjoining me to follow her ('Come with me, little slut, you'll make some *conversation*, your specialty'). The city driver made sure that all the other cars were lined up, and we headed toward Ostia. Just in those months Nanni Moretti's *Dear Diary* had been released in theaters, and at one point he makes the same journey, from Rome to the Idroscalo, on his Vespa—a film clip that has justly become famous, a solitary and liberating spiritual exercise. Laura, having brayed orders all morning, was shut in an impenetrable, turtle-like silence, interrupted only by some huffing. We proceeded south in the traffic. A little beyond the pyramid of Caio Cestio, with its white marble surfaces clothed in a dark patina of pollution, we passed Biondo Tevere, the restaurant where, the night of the crime, Pasolini had stopped to buy dinner (spaghetti with garlic and oil, and chicken breast, the trial transcripts report) for Pino Pelosi, called the Frog, still a minor the night of November 1, 1975. P.P.P., who had already dined in another restaurant (da Pommidoro, in San Lorenzo), had had a beer, watching the boy eat and finding out about his life, his desires, his opinions. The owners of the place knew him well, they called him respectfully 'the professor.' Were they alone, the boy and the poet, or was someone (sitting in a car with the engine off? on a motorcycle?) waiting for them to come out, tailing them from the gardens of Piazza dei Cinquecento, where P.P.P. had picked up Pino in his car? Of all the unresolved mysteries of that night, this is the most difficult to comprehend, and probably the key to all the rest. Might P.P.P. not have been drawn into a kind of trap, patiently plotted for weeks? In that case, nothing could have played the role of the hook better than the original reels of the last film, *Salò or the 120 Days of Sodom*, stolen some weeks earlier. Whatever thread of the tangle of that night is pulled, it always seems impossible, in the end, that Pelosi was the sole and solitary author of the crime, and of the plots that preceded it. And yet that is the truth contained in the verdict. On that now distant afternoon in March, 1994, the official truth concerning the homicide of P.P.P., in spite of its ridiculous contempt for the evidence, sat tranquil and imperturbable as a tyrant in his castle. The power of an official truth *never* lies in the fact that someone believes it. If one wanted to tell the story of the notorious *Italian character*, there might be no better basis than these conventional truths, which require no inner acceptance. One might go so far as to think that, the more illogical and almost intentionally inadequate such truths, the more effective they are: so as to highlight, rather than their laughable contents, the violence that establishes and sustains them. In fact, no one has ever seriously believed that it was Pelosi by himself who killed Pasolini, kicking and hitting him with a stick, then crushing him with his car, a gray Alfa GT, until his heart and his thoracic cavity, as the autopsy established, literally *burst*. It's a joke that makes no sense. But an official truth—I must insist on this point—is useful to everything except being believed. Let's be frank: its lacunae and open contradictions, far from making difficulties, only reinforce its threatening prestige—they are, so to speak, its royal diadem. A power that truly wants to inspire awe has to display a certain degree of illogic, because its roots sink into the Invisible, the Debatable, the Uncertain. Everything that the stubborn will of a minority restores to the light of day, including the eventual truth, is confined to the range of hypotheses. And hypotheses, as everyone knows, are the most perishable thing that human intelligence produces: they get worn out even in the mind of those who maintain them, they pile up, they contradict themselves. Even when they can boast a rigor similar to that of mathematical theorems, nothing removes them from their inevitable entropy.

To return to the metaphor of the tyrant, hypotheses are a crowd that you can easily shoot at. What might happen, on the other hand, is that the tyrant, locked in his castle, dies a natural death. For a long period no one is aware of it, and fear continues to rule as if nothing had occurred. But then, perforce, the chain vanishes. There's no longer danger in saying things that would, at other moments, have been paid for with death. But if there is no danger, there's often no longer any point in saying those things. Exactly thirty years after the night of the Idroscalo, the single person sentenced for homicide, Pino Pelosi, declared on TV that P.P.P. was murdered by two people, with heavy Sicilian accents; as for him, he remained on the sidelines of the fracas. In essence, it seems to me a version of the facts, if not credible in an absolute sense, more credible than all the preceding versions, and for a very particular reason. In 2005, those who for thirty years had kept the official truth from being seriously ousted from its throne (even though its absurdity and bad faith appeared obvious) are dead, or if they are still alive they are old and addled, incapable of doing harm. They can no longer threaten the lives of Pelosi or his family. Like all lowlifes, Pino the Frog is a man habituated to lying; but for that very reason he also knows perfectly when there is no need to lie anymore. To return to the day of the trip to the Idroscalo, it was still the time when those who knew were silent; and—one has to remember—had very good reasons to be silent. The caravan arrived at a crude fence beside the road, not far from the sea. To enter the small area you had to climb over a wooden gate of the type you'd find on a ranch in the Far West. The key had been forgotten, or the lock was too rusty. With more or less agility, we all contrived to perform that unexpected gymnastic exercise. Laura inserted herself between two boards of the gate, which fatally immobilized her, and she hung there, complaining, half in and half out, like an expressionist version of Winnie the Pooh in search of honey, stuck in the tree trunk. I recall Bernardo Bertolucci and a photographer from *Messaggero* engaged in a laborious effort of lifesaving. With the little drama resolved, we set out toward the monument, avoiding the garbage and the bushes withered by the salt air. As I was saying, it was early spring, one of those days when the light changes from minute to minute, with astonishing rapidity and inexhaustible imagination. Like a school of big fish, the violet clouds traveled swiftly across the sky, toward the city to the north. Gusts of wind filled our nostrils with the salty smell of the nearby sea. The sun, when it was free, spilled its almost dazzling gold onto that bleak and martyred no man's land. It was a glorious light, erupting from the openings in the clouds with the majesty of sacred music. It evoked the end of time, release from uncertainties, a supreme and unattainable quality of knowledge. But at a certain point, maybe because sunset still came early, maybe because the wind from the sea had fallen, reining in the course of the clouds, a livid shadow, of a cold purple, took over. A unanimous shudder went through the small crowd. No speeches or other ceremonies had been planned, the photographers had done their job, and each of us seemed to have arrived there without any agreement with the others, at the end of a solitary walk. Unmoving in the sky, its center dark, like a belly full of rain, the big cloud that loomed over us promised nothing good. And yet, looking in the direction of Fiumicino or Rome, the spring sky continued undisturbed its games of light. 'Let's go,' the Madwoman finally decreed, releasing the motley expedition. '*It's like being in the shadow of a corpse.*'

The Pasolini Foundation: one of those Roman apartments which, whether destined to the flow of a tedious life or to equally tedious business activities ('office use', as the real estate ads say), exude an unmistakable, irremediable atmosphere of repression and unhappiness. A desperate propriety from the time of Umberto I, a quiet but insistent instigation to suicide. A long corridor led off from the entrance, which was dominated by a giant copying machine. Through the first door on the left, which was always open, one entered (if one was forced to) the office of the Madwoman, enveloped in a constant, almost solid fog of cigarettes. Farther on, also on the left, was the audiovisual room, with the precious copies of Pasolini's films taken directly from the negatives. On the right, the bathroom. And at the end of the hall was a large reading room, which had shelves crammed with dusty folders and a big wooden file cabinet with small drawers. A place, in other words, identical to thousands of others—complete with hours open to the public, ancient iron radiators, windows with heavy frames opening to the outside. But this normality, as I perceived from my first days, was only an appearance. Even more occasional visitors realized it, without being able to explain why. In general they complained of an indefinable restlessness, a persistent difficulty in concentrating. And, obviously, they blamed themselves. They didn't suspect that that place endowed with all the proper trappings of reality, on the third floor of a massive, sullen building in the center of Rome, which housed various insurance firms, lawyers' and notaries' offices, and even a police station, had undergone an invisible but radical process of transformation. You had only to ring the bell and cross the threshold to find yourself inside an elsewhere in which the laws of the world had been deformed and, finally, suspended. Time and space no longer did their duty, or did it intermittently. I mean that the foundation's offices had become, in a process of absorption that had spared not even a doorframe or a tile, a *psychic space*—the extension of Laura's diseased and unhappy mind. Its habitability, as can be easily imagined, improved in the periods when the Madwoman, involved in a film or some other business, was away. A pale joy spread through the rooms of the foundation that was merely, in the end, a momentary relief. The snail, to use the most effective image I can think of, had so deeply saturated that shell with its humors that even when it went away the madness continued its unstoppable ooze. That places exist that are literally *infested* is not a simple gothic fantasy, an innocuous narrative expedient. We never lack, if we are attentive, occasions suitable for verifying the immense and devastating power of a dolorous and angry character hurled at full speed beyond the confines of the reality principle. Just as murderers and victims scatter their DNA over the scene of the crime, the mind possesses active energies that perhaps someday the scientific police will be able to discover by applying strict and indisputable protocols. What purification rite, I wondered, would be effective enough to neutralize such a palpable, intrusive influence as that exercised by the Madwoman? At times I imagined shamans, guardians in traditional outfits, with feather headdresses and bones in their noses, who danced up and down through the mournful rooms of the foundation calling on all their traditional remedies, reciting formulas and prayers, burning incense, drawing magic signs on the walls. The Madwoman's absences, anyway, never lasted very long. There she is, even more frightening than the last time you saw her, while in just a few minutes the temperature of unease regains its usual level. Those were the worst moments: because nothing had gone as it should have gone, no instruction had been carried out properly, everything had ended in the usual *betrayals*, the usual *knife in the back*. The mice had danced the *quadrille* and the *foxtrot*, while the Cat was away. There was also something for me: the lazy, hypocritical, complacent little slut. As I've mentioned, every day I could have decided not to return to that cage made of the same substance as the lunatic it held. I knew perfectly well that I was wasting my time; that an edition of Pasolini interviews edited by me would never see the light; that it was unlikely that I could take advantage of the materials preserved in the foundation to learn something. And yet, with a constancy I didn't think I possessed, I was there every morning, repeating from the beginning again the lesson of my nullity. The more I disgusted Laura, the more I found it absolutely necessary to hang around her, exposed to every sort of reprisal. To the hours in the office, she soon began adding an unpredictable amount of overtime. Willingly, during the lunch break, I followed her into some restaurant in the neighborhood of

Piazza Cavour. There was one, in particular, a kind of traditional *osteria* at the start of Via Crescenzio, where she was fond of the breaded anchovies. She could devour entire plates of them, with a feral rapture that quickly turned into a blind compulsion. Among all the behavioral disorders originating in nervous problems, those connected to food are the most striking, because they are based on a natural need, which they distort, and which is continually reappearing. I had never even distantly conceived that one could invite someone to lunch out of the desire to insult him while enjoying the pleasures of the table. But the only virtue that Laura attributed to me was that of managing to be—for lack of something better—a modest *lady-in-waiting*. It was a role, in her opinion, tailor-made for my cowardly bourgeois nature. Not coincidentally, she never failed to note, I aspired to a *literary career*—the form of existence most despised by P.P.P., who, of course, wouldn't have deigned even to look at someone like me. Not necessarily, I would respond, just to provoke her, P.P.P. was a cultivated man, he had respect and admiration for many writers. Without even confessing it to himself completely, he placed great value on the judgment of his peers. Who knows, he might even have taken a fancy to someone like me ... From the murkiest corner of the Madwoman's unfathomable guts, her sinister, hoarse laugh erupted (to provoke it in a public place like a restaurant could cost a remarkable embarrassment). '*YOU, with your perfumed little cunt?!? Pier Paolo would have vomited on it!!!*' Many people who knew Laura heard equally definitive and humiliating judgments, pronounced, as if carrying out a mandate, in the name of the specter of P.P.P. You'd disgust him, he wouldn't consider you worthy of writing about him, you don't understand a word of what he said. In her perpetual war against the human race, that certainly was the Madwoman's preferred weapon. An obviously childish trick, which reason could have easily neutralized. But, as we all know, reason, in this type of situation, has very limited prerogatives. The fact is that an unwanted psychological bond was established, through the mediation that Laura claimed for herself, between P.P.P. and the blameless, humiliated representatives of a human race incapable of measuring up to him. That mystification was effective even with the most astute and skeptical people. She possessed, in other words, a plausibility of her own. I will try to explain. I don't think that P.P.P. ever felt for any reason superior to others. I can't swear to it, since I never knew him, but over time I got an idea of him as a timid and serious man, endowed with that 'expertise in humility,' as Contini perfectly described it, which is a quality even rarer and more precious than humility itself. He was, above all, beyond any reasonable prudence, an absolutely genuine individual— and therefore able to arrive at a sort of limit, to transform his entire existence into a manifestation of the truth. 'To be *true*, and simply *true*, is the only thing that matters,' Stendhal wrote somewhere. That could be a perfect synthesis of the life and character of P.P.P. Unfortunately, it's very difficult for us, if not impossible, to consider such a beautiful human matter for what it was. A singular event, it's worth saying, and unique, that we should look at with the same disinterest needed to enjoy a work of art. A Titian portrait, a Chopin nocturne will never reproach us for not being like them. The life and work of P.P.P., on the contrary, always produce the perverse effect of an examination of conscience.

Completely unbeknownst to him and in spite of himself, P.P.P. has become, in memory and in the collective consciousness, better and better at making people feel guilty, a kind of pointing finger. Someone who compels his readers to confront their own cowardice, their fear of life, their enslavement. Of all useless activities, that type of examination of conscience, based on a comparison with one's neighbor, is undoubtedly the most useless. To return to the Madwoman, there is no doubt that she was very skillful at transforming that mistake into a subtle instrument of psychological torture. Subtle and effective, as I can testify myself, partly because it could be easily adapted to individual situations. There are some who tend to feel guilty about things that to others are totally indifferent. But almost everyone has an Achilles' heel. As for me, people endowed with the *vitality* of P.P.P. have always filled me with a mixture of admiration, uneasiness, inadequacy. Whatever the flames that burned him, Pasolini was on fire, he never stopped. He constructed an immense body of work with the most disparate artistic means, using indifferently a line of poetry or a wide-angle lens or a brush dipped in India ink, being photographed by others, giving interviews. And, then, there was the night, the moment when he turned his back on everyone, on the whole city, to walk alone, the hardened old hunter, in search of pleasure. He returned home very late, when not a soul is stirring, his steps echo on the cobblestones, the traffic signals blink. Via Eufrate, where he lived with his mother and a cousin, is in EUR, on the southernmost edge of the city, just before the plain that goes to the sea. There was a spur that goaded him, tormented his flesh and spirit in the same way, consumed him, and it was a spur of gold, a blessing, because it made his whole life, unconditionally, worth living, while the majority of his fellow-men rotted in prudence, keeping their distance. Laura, with her extremely powerful radar for the weaknesses of others, had intuited from the start that this was precisely my problem: standing apart, with the perpetual certainty that I wasn't really living, not really living to the full. 'You don't exist, little slut, and how could you? You were never born!! You're too much of a PHONY. And what would you want to write? *What do you know* about what you'd write?' Bull's-eye. It's true, I had worked so hard on my first book, stubbornly, seeking the right music, the rhythm of every single sentence. From twenty to thirty, I was preoccupied solely with learning to *write well*. I didn't know how else to define that so exclusive, so demanding preoccupation. But at a certain point you wake up and wonder if that's *really* all. The truth is that each of us, with some trouble, can learn to use the inks most suitable for performing our petty task, and call ourself a writer. But in the true inkwell, the one the great use, very different materials are bubbling: blood and sperm and fecal material and all the other unnamable muds where desires and aspirations and memories swarm, more vast and obscure than any word, than any convention. No matter how much I sharpened the nib of my pen I couldn't dip it in there. And that was why I was sure that the Madwoman, that impossible being, that living punishment, had something valuable to teach me, something that I couldn't go on pretending to ignore forever.

If we are all members of a single body, then there is no man or woman; or rather there are both: it's an androgynous or hermaphrodite body, which contains both sexes.

NORMAN O. BROWN, *Love's Body*

Like all truly important ideas, the idea for *Petrolio* arrived suddenly, one day between the spring and summer of 1972, suggested by the chance reading of the word *petrolio* ('petroleum') in a newspaper article. 'In less than an hour' Pasolini had scribbled an outline, the architecture of a story. He didn't remain completely faithful to that plan, but the essential is there, on that single sheet of paper. *Something written* tells a story, an adventure that takes place in Italy, between 1960 and the early seventies. But right from the start the story has the tone of a vision, of a hallucination, of a revelatory dream. Right away the so-called real world appears transfigured by a metaphysical light, pervaded by omens and teachings. In the beginning there is a man, A. His name is Carlo, Carlo Valletti. He's a progressive intellectual, an engineer, an expert in petroleum research. As is typical of his class, he seems not to possess a body; his body has been totally swallowed up by his intelligence and his ambition. Well, this man at a certain point divides in two: A produces B, like Dr. Jekyll and Mister Hyde. This second Carlo is a comic shadow of the first, a meek, innocent being, always excited, always hunting for pleasure with every type of woman, from girls to grandmothers. The division of labor is perfect. Assigned to 'low services,' Carlo the Second allows Carlo the First, the petroleum engineer, to attend to his career without fear of scandals, to lead an irreproachable life. For a long time, the equilibrium and the agreement between the two Carlos are perfectly maintained. Pasolini very much liked this sort of fantasy. Once, some years earlier, he had written that doubling, the dividing of a single person into two, is 'the greatest of literary inventions.' If you think about it carefully, it might even be true. But at the moment when he writes the outline of *Petrolio*, doubling doesn't in the least use up all the possibilities of the character. The prodigy produces a new prodigy. *The double produces the androgyne.* In the beginning, working on the first draft, Pasolini thought that only Carlo the Second was to become a woman, shortly before the other, engineer Valletti, made an important trip to the Middle East for work. Remaining alone in Rome, 'and furthermore a woman,' Carlo the Second would devote himself to 'low services' with the usual ardor, but, as a consequence of his new sex, he would start seeking males. Writing *Petrolio*, Pasolini realized that both of his heroes had to become women, at a certain point, and later return to being men. The stakes of these metamorphoses, in fact, are enormous. As happens in the most archaic and secret layers of mythical thought, androgyny is the sign, the specific condition of a dizzying *increase in knowledge*, of a possession of the world that, through the catastrophe of the old identity, makes possible the metamorphosis, the initiation into a superior regime of truth.[5] The right standard for deciphering Pasolini's last book is not that of literature, of novelistic invention. *Something written*, from the moment of its conception, is a sacred book, an announcement, a revelation. The supernatural exploits of its allegorical puppets refer to a process that is under way, a truth that is happening. It's this type of authenticity that Pasolini throws in the face of his readers when he declares that he is *living* the genesis of *Petrolio*.

Petrolio was there before me, waiting to be deciphered. Its nature as a mysterious object, its unmistakable vibration as a supreme message made it different from any other book I had encountered. But how to enter into it? What was the key to its code? Once, Alfred Hitchcock wanted to put a particular dramatic accent on an object in one of his shots, a glass that contained poisoned milk. But it was too small and too ordinary to grab the viewer's attention by itself. And so he had a stroke of genius: he put a light bulb in the glass of milk. It must be because of the white cover, but the Einaudi edition of *Petrolio* reminded me of Hitchcock's famous glass of milk. As this resembled countless other glasses, so *Petrolio*, in many ways, belonged to a recognizable set of books: it was a work of the late twentieth century, a perfect example of a unique era of freedom and exploration in all fields of art. Yes: but there was something more. The light that pulsed inside it, if you could perceive it, gave off a message of solitude, of looming threat, of a terminal stage of experience. A great deal of ink has been spilled on the last years of Pasolini (from around fifty on), obviously. But it always ends up in the same formulas, which are ultimately merely paraphrases of remarkable concepts expressed by the subject himself in *Corsair Writings* and in *Lutheran*

Letters. Altogether, the critical writing on Pasolini is one of the most boring creations of the human spirit. Everything is reduced to sociological and psychological formulas that are so watered-down they could apply to everyone and everything. About one thing, then, one couldn't say that the Madwoman was wrong. No one understood anything about *Petrolio* at the moment of its publication. The articles that came out in the papers were so superficial that very often they talked about great scenes of homosexual love, without even realizing that the protagonist had become a woman. Then that other idea prevailed, that *Petrolio* was a sort of roman-à-clef, in which P.P.P. had stepped on the toes of too many powerful people. But that's not why, for this or that reason, *Petrolio* is a unique, irreplaceable work. *Something written* is not exactly a text, understood as an object that, sooner or later, must separate from its author. If anything it's a shadow, a trace, the fever chart hanging at the foot of the bed. It wouldn't make sense if there weren't someone delirious between the sheets. What Pasolini does in *Petrolio* is closer to body art than to literature. Or even to photography. Nosing around in the materials at the foundation, I happened to come across the photographs of P.P.P. that Dino Pedriali had taken, in Sabaudia and Chia, in October of 1975, two weeks before his death. At the time Pasolini was fifty-three, thirty years older than Pedriali. After an initial distrust, a perfect understanding arose between the two, as one can easily sense from the beauty of the result. Pedriali's photographs are like a story, clearly divided into two parts—the first at Sabaudia, and the second in the medieval tower in Chia, where P.P.P. had a country house. This second part is the more beautiful and intense, and culminates in a series of splendid nudes. Pedriali maintains—and there's no reason to doubt it—that Pasolini asked him not to publish the photos in newspapers and magazines, because he intended to put them in the book he was writing, as an integral part of the work. Pasolini wasn't able to see those photos, because by the time Pedriali had finished developing and printing them he was dead. But what we see in these illuminating images is, without a shadow of a doubt, that man of 'flesh and blood' who is writing *Petrolio*. He's a man who has arrived, one might say, at the extreme limit of individual fulfillment. It's impossible to be more fully oneself than this. After photographing him at work at a big table of rough wood, correcting a typescript with a pen, and crouching on the floor, drawing on big sheets of paper, Pedriali leaves the house, while Pasolini, in the bedroom, shows himself totally naked to the gaze of someone who, from outside, seems to spy on him through the windowpane, in which the reflections of the trees are printed. Thin and muscular, with his big penis hanging between his legs, the poet reads a book, sitting in a chair beside the bed or lying on the white quilt. He seems to have no age, or to be all ages at once. For a while he pretends not to realize that he is being looked at. But then the game seems boring to him, and he, too, starts looking through the glass, toward the position of the viewer. He has now stood up, and seems to be trying to make out something in the darkness of the night. I'm here, he seems to say, I'm here now, and this double-edged blade, this being looked at, which is also the last occasion for looking, is all that remains. And there is no greater risk than that run by one who accepts that he is nothing but himself, 'in flesh and blood,' like an animal, a god, a man sentenced to death.

All human encounters, even and especially the most absurd, have the power to awaken the dilettante moral philosopher and the third-rate psychologist that are lurking in us. Considered as an object for study, Laura Betti required an intellectual investment no less than that which I devoted to *Petrolio*. Had the Madwoman always been like that—filled with that unnamable suffering, that blind and cosmic malevolence? Or, at a certain point in her life, had something particular (the death of P.P.P., for example, or an awareness of getting old, or even an obscure, unmotivated depression that she had harbored for years) inflicted an irreparable blow? When it was all over, I wavered on the horns of a dilemma. Traumas, undoubtedly, occur. But the sum of sufferings and sorrows that befall us through the sole fact of being alive, all endurable if considered singly, might be enough itself to crush us, like roofs under the weight of a snowfall that lasts too long. And if we observe with a certain degree of attention and empathy the most disconcerting mutations of a character, sooner or later we are forced to admit that they correspond to tendencies and peculiarities that have always been there, like beasts hiding in the shadows, muscles tensed, ready to strike. I questioned people who had known Laura when she was young. They poured out anecdotes, by the dozen. But the protagonists of the particular narrative form that is the anecdote are always personages, not persons: masks from an eternal social commedia dell'arte attached to phrases and gestures that may be memorable but are always extraneous to the nucleus, the primary core of the character. Especially since the majority of these anecdotes came from the bottomless pit of the Dolce Vita, with all its frills, its caricatures, its faintly rancid odor of cultural-worldly legend. Always the same stuff, slightly soporific: Via Veneto, the bars of Piazza del Popolo, Cinecittà. La Giaguara, the Jaguar—so Laura, in those roaring years, had been christened by some magazine, as opposed to Ornella Vanoni, la Mangusta, the Mongoose. She had moved to Rome from Bologna in the late fifties, just in time to immerse herself in the great melting pot, soon becoming a standard ingredient. She had changed to Betti (apparently on the advice of Luchino Visconti) her much more prosaic family name, Trombetti. Her first house, in Via del Babuino, had become a celebrated refuge of well-known night revelers. There Pasolini, too, arrived one evening, dragged by Goffredo Parise. He was shy and silent amid that cynical, loquacious, cutting intellectual Roman worldliness that always roused in him feelings of both disgust and fear. At the time of that first encounter, P.P.P. was still in his thirties. One day when she was in the mood for reminiscence, and I had asked her something about it, Laura said she had immediately realized that that man was *different from all the others*. A kind of skinny, bespectacled god, she had added, visiting a world of shits, and preoccupied solely with finding a way of turning back as quickly as possible. One can find a reliable description of the Jaguar's house in Via del Babuino, and of the humanity that frequented it, in *Breve Vita di Pasolini* (Brief Life of Pasolini), by Nico Naldini. I quote it in detail, not only because it's a firsthand testimony but also because Naldini's perspective is definitely malicious. Among all the human arts, none is so far from objectivity and neutrality as that of the portrait, whether written or painted. And sentiments like hatred, rancor, or even disgust—provided they're not pointlessly censored—can turn out to be tools of knowledge more refined than love or admiration.

Laura, Naldini recounts, 'had sacrificed well-being to a career as a singer-actress in Rome. A refined singer of music composed for her by well-known composers, with words by well-known literary types. But she had no breath and as an actress was hardly better than a character actor. She had found the great actress in herself in a talent for imaginative associations, in the impulses of a character straining to cultivate contrasts. The show took place in her first Roman house, in Via del Babuino. Lying on a big bed, draped in bright-colored flowing gowns to hide her obesity, she controlled, with voice and gestures, the rules of a court of her own invention where everything was permitted and everything derided. When you arrived in Via del Babuino you entered freely into a space decorated with ostrich and peacock feathers, antique and other hats bought at the flea market, cascades of pearls. It foreshadowed a future style of décor. The house, all the way to the foot of the bed, was open to everyone along the chain of friends down to the prostitutes who arrived in the entourage of Franco Rosellini and, when Laura was absent, occupied the famous bed, leaving traces of their passage. One day the cleaning woman said to her: "I found stuff for homosexuals in the bed." In that house you could run into a half naked lesbian duchess and the instructions were not to take her for a sailor. Even Marlon Brando showed up, who liked sinking into the pillows, one on top of the other in a hypothetical ascension to a Tibet of silk.'

As for the Jaguar's talent, however, Naldini's judgment seems to me excessively harsh. It's also possible that the breath wouldn't have helped her much; but she should be credited with a personal style, immediately recognizable— in itself a rare gift, almost more difficult to find among singers than among writers or painters. Talent, besides, is the most skillful of illusionists—and the strongest move in its repertory consists precisely in transforming limitations into points of strength. From Arbasino to Flaiano, from Calvino to Parise and P.P.P. himself, all or almost all the most important writers of the time composed texts for the Jaguar to sing. From this emerged a legendary show, entitled *Giro a vuoto* (Walking in Circles*)*. In 1962, a French version was performed in Paris. Among the spectators there was a man of about sixty, who loudly expressed his enthusiasm. Not recognizing him, Laura had thought he was a heckler. In fact it was André Breton, who lived near the Comédie de Paris, in Rue Fontaine, the theater where the performance took place. The author of *Nadja*, who was extremely sensitive to every form of psychological deviance, couldn't remain insensitive to the call of the Jaguar. With the enthusiasm of the true connoisseur, who has just enriched his collection with a rare and valuable object, he let Laura extort a brief encomium, inspired by the most unconditional admiration. 'If you have never seen a tempest in a glass of water (not in the figurative sense but in the physical meaning of the term) what are you waiting for? What are you waiting for to go and applaud Laura Betti in what she calls, certainly with irony, her *Giro a vuoto*?' Breton has no doubts: Rimbaud, when he spoke of 'the gay poison of the convolvulus,' had glimpsed something similar. 'If each of her songs marvelously enfolds her, it's because it's one with her, it's because the song is forged of the same fire that she inhabits. She is inseparably the inspiration and the interpreter. The lyricists model their lines on a flash of her eyes, on a black rose that slides dizzily off her knee.'

Breton was absolutely right: in the case of Laura the tempest in the glass of water was not an innocuous locution but a real, 'physical' phenomenon, concretely observable. Considered as glasses, we are all fated to tolerate our tempests more or less happily. In some specimens of this large set of glasses that is humanity, however, the wave motion does not know pauses, rhythms of calm and agitation. In other words, there are individuals who live their whole life in a constant state of emergency, a state of exception.[6] A destiny? A calculated choice? A game that finally becomes a kind of uncontrollable compulsion? In any case, there is always something *tyrannical* in a disturbed nature that puts it at the center of attention. Especially when its basic tendencies are challenge, provocation, perpetual fighting. That was what the Madwoman liked most of all: to say fuck off, to unearth on the spot the most vicious and offensive thing she could do or say to whoever was there. She was a 'shit' character, as Goffredo Fofi described her with precision, 'so intolerable that she roused a homicidal instinct in the meekest.' As the years passed things only got worse; but already at the time of the house on Via del Babuino—the witnesses are in agreement—the Jaguar had made aggression her rule of life. She adhered to it as to a monastic vow. It should immediately be added that all this had not ostracized her. On the contrary. In that artistic-intellectual Roman world where she had settled, with her quick tongue and her easy virtue, the rules were respected as in a puppet theater. And then Laura possessed an extraordinary and disarming capacity to vary her register. In certain circumstances, the Madwoman left the field to the Good: an understanding friend, almost too solicitous, capable of attention and genuine sympathy, generous with advice. This metamorphosis, sudden and completely unpredictable, could last several hours, even an entire day. But you had to be careful not to trust it, not to fall for it. At any moment, that new personality could melt like snow in the sun. Not before, however, having produced its insidious effects. Because that person who was so pleasant, understanding, attentive to your needs truly existed: she was there, before your eyes, fragile and disarming like everything that possesses a genuine kindheartedness. And so there must also have been a method (a certain orderly sequence of words, for example, or of gestures, or of tiny events) of extracting that unpredictable variation from the dark, sinister, seething matter that was Laura's habitual character. But you had to give in to it. The benign aspect was a mask, donned on a whim at an unpredictable moment. It didn't reveal any more genuine layer of awareness, or of character. As soon as you began to enjoy it, the new blow hit you, and all you could do was admit that you had been cheated yet again. The fact is that the Madwoman, as long as those extemporaneous *exercises in kindness* lasted, identified completely with the new role. And those who were around during those intervals enjoyed in effect the company of an intelligent and perceptive person, able to listen to her neighbor, endowed with an enviable experience of the world and a taste that was anything but common. I, too, had the experience, and much more often than might have been predicted from her normal attitude of hostility and recrimination toward me. Half an hour earlier she might have reduced you to ashes with all the force of her fantastic insults, and now, wrapping herself in an enormous cloak, she would ask you, as if only exquisite compliments passed between you and her, to go with her somewhere. And why not? The first time I met Laura the Good we were in an old wig store in the neighborhood of Teatro Argentina. She needed a pair of brown, wavy locks for a film she was to shoot. Some final adjustments were required, and so the owner of the workshop, who had known Laura for a long time, had invited us to sit down in a waiting room. Dozens of polystyrene heads, with the facial features barely sketched above long necks, were arranged on long shelves, displaying a sample book of wigs of every shape and color. It seemed a de Chirico fantasy, made even more disquieting by the big mirrors that multiplied to infinity those mute, severe companions of ours. Laura held in her lap the cup from the coffee someone had brought her, to use as an ashtray, which was soon overflowing. The conversation had turned to some of her old loves: Claudio Villa (who 'had a really big one'), Tomas Milian (stolen in defiance of Zeffirelli, possibly the handsomest man she had ever met), a very rich landowner who if he had married her would have made her the owner 'of at least three-quarters of the Prosecco drunk in Italy.' At times we think we're leafing through an innocent album of memories, just to pass the time, and instead it's a dangerous Pandora's box that we are handling recklessly. A dark melancholy first embittered Laura's voice, then broke and weakened it almost to weeping. It wasn't a sudden attack of nostalgia for Claudio Villa, or for the Paduan prince of Prosecco, that shook her so deeply. Nor was it general regret for a golden age that had passed forever, too long ago. Like a foot that unexpectedly sinks into treacherous soil, so the mind, believing it's proceeding without risk amid slight regrets and minor sufferings, can hurtle, without a how or a why, into the Great Despair, where life appears for what it is, without veils, without euphemisms: a gigantic swindle, a bank that always wins in the end, leaving you without even a coin to bet. It was there, at the bottom of that well, that I saw Laura become upset, with all the threads of conversation by now broken. Like archaic Mothers, Mediterranean goddess-guardians of death and fate, the bewigged polystyrene heads seemed to nod on their shelves. Her elbow resting on the arm of the chair that she had sunk into, and barely contained her, Laura extended a hand toward me, sitting next to her. It was natural, as an immediate reaction, to think that she would hit me. I was wrong. I would never in a million years have guessed her real intentions, which were to pet me, just as one does a cat. I didn't mind that unprecedented form of contact, even if I couldn't think of an evident reason for it. Some minutes passed like that, the Madwoman lost in her grief, and I submissive to her will. If I had been capable of it, I would even have started purring, just to please her. 'Maybe you're not all wrong, little slut, to always keep *to yourself,* she whispered, finally, sniffing, and staring at me as if she were seeing me for the first time. 'Because life, at a certain point ... cuts the cord ... *with its full load* ... you understand me? No, you don't understand, what can you know about it. And you stay like that, with one hand in front and the other behind ... given that something of a sense of modesty still matters to you ... ' How to say she was wrong? Judging from the results I was facing, there were neither euphemisms nor consolations available. Look at her there, the mangy, shabby Jaguar, suffocated by her very obesity, betrayed and disappointed, with no more hope to warm her endgame. What remained to her, apart from food and cigarettes? Was it the famous Sunset Boulevard? The image was too sentimental. It would have been better to speak of a collapse, a devastation more like a natural disaster than like a process perhaps painful but explicable in rational terms. The worst was still to come, in this catastrophic balance. Sooner or later, I had a presentiment, her tongue would worry the tooth that hurt. Suddenly, I realized that the ghost of P.P.P. had been there with us, as we waited for the adjustments to be made to the wigs. It seemed to me that I almost saw him, sitting on the other side of the room, or nestled in one of the infinite reflections of the mirror, the heavy-framed eyeglasses, a tight-fitting leather jacket, hands crossed on his knees. As if we shared the exact same illusion, Laura looked in that direction. 'Pier Paolo ... when I met him, was no longer a boy... but he still had certain manners that were so *timid* ... Just the opposite of me. That's why we had such a good time. I shouted, was provocative. He, sometimes, with certain people, there was no way to make him utter a word ... But he had such a *presence* ... no, there's never been a man like him. Where he was, now there's a void, and that void *shouts*, it won't stop shouting ... You know, in the last period—I know it's easy to say, but it's really true—I realized that something wasn't right. He was keeping me distant. In *Salò* he didn't want Ninetto or me. It's true that

I was making another film, but that's not the point. He said he wanted to protect me. The fascists, the secret services. One day everything will come out. When they're all dead. You'll be able to read the story in the newspapers, in books. But even in that case ... it's not as if everything can be written. In the last days, he was there ... and he wasn't there: at the same time, in the same situation ... he was there, and he was somewhere else. And it was difficult to be with him, because, sooner or later, it seemed to you that you *didn't exist*.' The bitter pill, the saddest bitter pill, in the end was spit out. And the surest proof that Laura had really loved P.P.P., to the limits of her capacity to love, receiving almost nothing in exchange, lay precisely in that sensation, as naked and precise as a scientific report, of *not existing*. Among all the sufferings that life forces us to bear, there may be no suffering greater than this: to love someone more than oneself, and to enjoy, up to a certain point, his presence—and at the same time to understand that that beloved being, while he is there with us, in flesh and blood, and shares his time with us, in reality belongs only to his own fate, which, even as we're sure we're holding him close, carries him far away. Because his story, no matter how hard we try, is not ours and never will be.

There's no escape—a life without love inevitably becomes something so withered and dusty, so desolate, so insignificant, that it's not even worth the trouble to talk about it. Let's think of a pair of dirty underpants forgotten under the bed in an abandoned house: there's an eloquent enough image of a life without love. In comparison, every type of broken heart is a lucky heart, which has played its part. If it was broken, it means that it lived; if it has lived, it means that it has had its moments of joy. As for breaking into pieces, it's the fate of all things. And so if it's obvious that the Madwoman's love for P.P.P. had been, from every point of view, unhappy, like all unrequited loves, it's equally indisputable that that unhappiness, whose existence the interested party didn't even suspect, or if he suspected couldn't care less about, was, ultimately, a great good fortune and a great resource. The current sense of the expression 'lucky in love' is completely mistaken, because it refers to a result that doesn't actually exist. Even if we killed and ate him (something that at times happens literally), the beloved being, for some elusive reason, will never be ours. He can give us his entire soul, or if you prefer his ass, he can give us both (letting us understand that, at most, it's the same thing), but there will always be a part of this being that escapes us, perhaps owing to the very fact that we love him, just as the piece of meat reflected in the river's current will always escape the dog in the fable. And so these blessed unhappy loves are merely a tautology, since all loves, being unable to pursue their purpose even at the price of torture and murder, are unhappy. What we can hope for, if anything, is to meet (without even deserving them) people who, instead of *properties* impossible to control, represent, for us, *adventures*. Pinocchio's best friend, remains, ultimately, Candlewick, and the most desirable fate that can befall us is to visit some Land of Toys that, as fools, we would never be able to get to on our own. And to wake up one fine morning with donkey ears is not at all the worst of evils. The worst of evils is to keep going straight along our own road of shit, thinking we are doing our duty. Like a seductive, irresistible Candlewick, P.P.P. transported Laura, that arrogant, rowdy Jaguar of Piazza del Popolo, that singer for intellectuals, that Bolognese of very easy virtue, to an elsewhere from which she would never be able to return completely, or completely whole. And, needless to say, she was right not to put up any resistance. That elsewhere, that Land of Toys where she let herself be transported, undergoing progressive and irreversible metamorphoses, has a very alluring characteristic, which consists in being neither completely true nor completely false. It's an intermediate world, subject to laws that are valid only within it. As will be intuited, I'm talking about the cinema. Pasolini often stressed the profound reasons for his fascination with this means of expression, which he got to know quite late, on the threshold of middle age. Not unlike the other arts, cinema is a code, let's say even a language—and therefore a tool, a device, a freedom. But the consonants and vowels of this language come directly, without mediation, from the womb of Reality. They are spaces, conditions of light, bodies of men and animals, dust, sweat. Whatever the intentions of the director are, his aesthetic or political convictions, his most inadmissible desires and hopes, that is his limitation, and at the same time his unprecedented freedom. On the other hand, this overdose of Reality doesn't necessarily imply a paralysis, an attitude of passivity. As the poet appropriates his mother tongue in a way so radical as to make us believe (and to believe himself) that he has invented it rather than inherited and learned it, and is the first to speak it, so the director manipulates, digs, dismantles the alphabet and the syntax of the world. And his authority is plain both in cases in which the intervention is obvious and prolonged, and in the more insidious cases, in which he declares he's letting go, giving up any form of control, acting like someone who is watching as if he had chanced to pass by there.[7] There can't be, in particular, work with the actor in which a will to power is not implicated—marked more or less, depending on the case, by aggression. As for P.P.P., the most fitting image for his way of working has always seemed to me that of the potter who makes his clay objects on the potter's wheel. The pressure may seem minimal, but it's what decides the shape, irreversibly. And in his career as a director, it has to be admitted, he faced materials much more resistant than Laura, who, in spite of her displays of bad behavior and rebellion, and all her jealous scenes, nevertheless always lived in a state of constant adoration and psychological submission toward him. Pasolini's energy was such that he managed to pry loose from their cavities high-carat gemstones like Orson Welles, Totò, Maria Callas—illuminating these figures from angles that no one had ever suspected. In comparison, poor Laura was a blank check. As she herself confided to Barth David Schwartz, the author of an ample biography of P.P.P., she wanted to stay near him 'forever,' without caring what she would receive in exchange, 'even at the cost of being like a puppy or a cat.' This devotion, which in her life caused her atrocious suffering, produced excellent results in the films. It will be enough to take a rapid tour through a gallery of memorable images: here's Laura in *Curd Cheese*, as a capricious diva accompanied by the starving dog. With whiskers, and armed with a camera, in *The Earth as Seen from the Moon*, where she plays the part of an English tourist visiting the Colosseum. And again: the blond Desdemona-puppet of *What Are the Clouds?*, with cherry-like earrings and extremely long fake eyelashes. And the Wife of Bath in *The Canterbury Tales*, as imposing as an allegorical sculpture on the portal of a Romanesque church. But an album of bizarre and picturesque images doesn't necessarily correspond to something truly important. In all the films I've cited, Laura was marginal, potentially replaceable. Nothing comparable to the character of Emilia, the servant in *Theorem*. This is the only time that P.P.P. worked as a director with the highest ambitions for Laura, and the results were an intense, luminous poetry.

Theorem was shot in Sant'Angelo Lodigiano, near Milan, in March of 1968—the light of an incipient, still cold Po Valley spring invades many of the film's scenes. Two months later, the world would no longer be the same. Laura was just over forty. But her character is outside of time, in the sense that she contains in herself, in every day of her silent and subdued life, all the ages of life. I quote Pasolini himself, who, also in the spring of 1968, with Garzanti, published *Theorem* as a book, a mixture of prose and verse: 'Emilia is an ageless girl, who could be eight or thirty-eight: a poor northern Italian; an outcast of the white race.' In the allegory of *Theorem*, that 'outcast of the white race,' in the service of a family of the industrial Milanese high bourgeoisie, has a crucial importance, which is revealed the first day a mysterious Guest turns up in the sumptuous villa in the Po Valley, surrounded by a splendid park. No different from her masters, Emilia, too, is riveted by the erotic allure of Terence Stamp. She's the first to make love with him, after he has prevented her from killing herself. Then the Guest will move on, inexorable and irresistible, to the entire family, excluding no one. But at the moment of his departure (which can't be put off, and is as inexplicable as his arrival) Emilia's destiny divides forever from that of the people she's served. The Guest, erupting into the family like a supreme and overpowering incarnation of desire, destroys its unity, and on his departure leaves behind a landscape in ruins. For Emilia the Guest's departure is a catastrophe: but in a very different sense. Between the divine (or diabolical?) invader and Emilia, the poor outcast, one of the 'dispossessed of the world,' there exists a mysterious 'complicity.' That makes the poor servant the true protagonist of the second part of the film (and of the book). While her masters, each confined in his own solitude, sink into desperation, vainly mourning the guest who has disappeared forever, for Emilia a new story begins, which leads her straight to holiness and a miracle. With her big cardboard suitcase, which contains all her possessions, she returns to the peasant world she came from. We see her living outside, in the courtyard of a big farmhouse, feeding on nettles, curing a child with boils, ascending to Heaven, arms spread, like a mystical wind rose of the Po. At the end, she will be buried in a construction site, where the bulldozers have dug a deep hole, the foundation of some new building or other. Her tears are the source of a miraculous fountain, which can heal wounds. What a great idea, what an ironic stroke of genius P.P.P. had when he decided to assign the part of Emilia to Laura. Between the actress and the mask that she would have to put on there was not a single point in common, no possible hook for identification. Sanctity and sub-proletarian humility were equally alien to that fearless exhibitionist, that artist of the grotesque, that bourgeoise from Bologna born into a cultured, anti-Fascist family, brought up to privilege from birth. It seems that everything, in life, can change, including vices and character—except for one's social class. In no case can that branding by fire be removed, whatever you do. But if what separates the actress and the character of Emilia had been only an abyss of a sociological nature, Pasolini's psychological experiment would be less than unusual. The fact is that Laura did not start off at a disadvantage only because of her background. Any actor can confront a problem like that, perhaps succeeding, thanks to his talent, in transforming the limitation into an advantage. But here we have a case of systematic, diametrical opposition. More than the prerogatives of the director, Pasolini seems to have exercised those of the alchemist, who forces his material into unprecedented metamorphoses. From the first scene, in other words, we witness the disconcerting, mesmerizing display of Laura advancing toward her opposite, as if she were swimming against a strong current, the current of her own identity, which doesn't allow her the tiniest instant of inertia. And that desperate labor, in the final analysis destined to failure, is a supreme artistic experience, something that anyone should fear but also—with the same intensity—hope for.

In 1971, three years after *Theorem*, Pasolini published in *Vogue* the *Necrologia di una certa Laura Betti* (Obituary of a Certain Laura Betti), a kind of macabre joke with a school-boyish flavor. Laura, without realizing the essential coldness of this document, was very fond of it, and reprinted the Obituary, in 1979, as the introduction to a muddled volume of memories and little stories of hers. P.P.P. imagines that his friend has died in 2001, thirty years later—a prediction that was short but only by a few years. From the first lines of this unsuccessful exercise, the author displays a certain impatience toward his subject, as if the sole fact of having undertaken the task of writing those two pages had put him in a bad mood. In other words, the tone is false throughout, as of one who intends to appear sympathetic and witty but in reality would like only to be left in peace. In spite of all that, these are still the thoughts of the intuitive, perceptive P.P.P. And one can't help feeling a shudder reading a couple of lines from the final epigraph, which have the character of an indisputable analysis: '*She grew old and died: but I'm sure that in her grave she feels like a child. She is certainly proud of her death, considering it a special death.*'

Life at the Pasolini Foundation, the time spent observing its habitués, the people who worked there, the Madwoman— aside from all that, it, too, was a world, and like all worlds was endowed with its particular illusion of vastness, of infinity. The warm, shadowy selective limbo of the classics in general exercises, if and when it can, an exclusively intellectual, bookish fascination. The case of P.P.P. was, and still is, completely different. I mean that his audience is more heterogeneous, not to say more ambiguous, than that which writers usually have. An enviable situation. Even today the readers of P.P.P. are a random mixture of serious scholars, disturbed subjects in search of identification, paranoids with their puzzles, artists in search of revelatory metaphors, politicians in search of purity, people who don't even know what they're looking for. In a cultural world as predictable and respectable as that of the Italian official left, which produced, more than anything else, boredom and a desire for escape, if not suicide, P.P.P.'s presence is essentially *equivocal*. All of that is inevitably reflected in the rooms of the foundation, where thoughtful people, with well-defined projects in mind, encountered the most solemn and complete idlers. Dragan and Ljuda, for example, belonged to the second category. They were from Sarajevo, and had had time to finish I don't know what school of theater directing before the war and the siege of their city began. They were young, around twenty-five. He was tall and large, with long black hair, she slender, with intensely green eyes and high cheekbones, a sensation of force and endurance spreading over her body like oil. They both wore combat boots and leather jackets. They had been in Venice, then in Milan, and now they were in Rome, because Laura, seized by one of her inexplicable moods of generosity, had taken them under her protection: finding them a house to stay in, belonging to a friend of hers who was in America, and trying to help them with a theater project inspired by *Salò* and *Petrolio*. That was why I had found them one morning camped out in the foundation reading room, and Laura had abruptly ordered me to help them in whatever research they had to do. In five minutes it was clear that they would not get very far with that so-called research. They knew English pretty well, but their Italian was rudimentary and above all they didn't care anything about anything, they were there only to please Laura. While they were still students, before the war, they had shot some scenes on a farm, a farm where geese were butchered. Even after the decapitation, when, in place of the head, there was only a stump, from which a dense jet of blood gushed, the geese continued walking, with their characteristic gait, at times traversing the entire length of the courtyard. These shots were to be the basis of their film on *Salò*. The title was *Goose Step*. Dragan and Ljuda would never have set foot again at the foundation, but during that first encounter we had become friends, and I often went to see them at night in the apartment they had settled in, in Trastevere. Certain couples exercise over me an attraction much more profound than anything that one of the two elements, considered singly, could. In those two, I liked that type of sensual neglect that only the Balkan peoples know the secret of. The world, one might say, was their ashtray. They drank and smoked until late, they slept in the morning, they let time pass. They had two TVs in the house, a big one in the living room and a smaller one on the fridge in the kitchen, and they kept both of them on. And on TV, in that winter of 1994, there was a constant flow of pictures of the siege of Sarajevo, which was in its third year—the longest siege of a city in a modern war. You could see the dark masses of the Serb cannons around the city, the gutted skyscrapers on the snipers' boulevard, the cemeteries on the slopes of the grassy hills, the contorted carcass of the tall building where *Oslobodjenje*, the city daily, continued to come out literally under the bombs. At a certain point, to the images of this frightening repertory was added that of the great library on the riverbank, completely incinerated: reduced to its slender skeleton, like a cage, or an old hatbox, and explored by packs of emaciated and freezing dogs. Everywhere in the world, from Canada to Italy and from Argentina to Germany, there were Bosnians, who were born and had grown up in Sarajevo, who every day watched on television the inexorable dissolution of their world, of their past. It was a mad and incomprehensible sight, the waking dream of a psychotic. Dragan and Ljuda, too, were shocked by it, as if every newscast eroded a bit of the ground beneath their feet. The images flowed and the TV remained on and we avoided talking about it, but sometimes I saw clearly the blow they had suffered. And yet something saved them; they had dug out a den, a world within the world. Ever since they were children, their *true life*—one could not call it anything else—had unfolded elsewhere, in semi-clandestine places, in houses of acquaintances, in villas outside the city. That the world around them was crumbling they could not not know. But until the last moment they read their underground magazines, drank beer, listened to their punk and heavy metal music. Yet the pivot was not the beer or the music, it was violence, it was all the rituals of violence, domination and submission, the steps and rules of both. They had gone through stages, they had learned. Like genuine initiates of a cult, they knew how to find in every city in the world, just by wanting to, other people like them. Seen from the outside, the sadomasochistic practices and philosophy could also seem like a load of nonsense, and maybe in themselves they were, but within that stuff a certain illumination was gained. There was a way of achieving the most difficult thing—that is, understanding one's own nature. Even if evoked in a kind of game that from the outside might seem garish, violence is violence, it doesn't take much to understand that. It's part of a primitive layer of being, and for that reason is bound to the sacred, to the not transitory—like orgasm, like the ecstasies of mystics. P.P.P. had passed through the same bottlenecks. *Salò* and *Petrolio* couldn't be considered simply as his last works. More than works, they were states of the organs. As if that film and that book, instead of being content with having been made and written like all the others, had sprouted in him, like wings or horns in a fable of metamorphosis. And that metamorphosis was based on violence: on submission, on being beaten, on deliberately provoking a violent reaction just as one evokes a deity, a sacred power. With all their ignorance, my Bosnian friends

or the Madwoman were much closer to those final truths of
P.P.P.'s than all the critics and scholars put together, with their
books and their interpretations. Sometimes the Madwoman
invited all three of us to dinner, at her house, in the heart of
Rome. She wanted to dine early and she cooked, as usual,
an immoderate quantity of food. It might happen that the
hostess didn't let out even a word. What strange, unpredictable company: the two exiles, the Madwoman, the eternal
apprentice idler. Those were the moments when the ghost
of P.P.P. seemed more real and present to me than the very
air I was breathing, than the noise of the city that, reduced
to a faint background, reached Laura's house, than the taste
of the food. Like a magnet, even from the other world, even
from underground P.P.P. continued to attract to himself his
iron filings. He united alien and distant destinies.

A decade earlier, in 1985, when I was still in university, the students of the Communist Youth League, as it was called in those distant times, had asked me to plan with them a kind of symposium on Pasolini. Exactly ten years had passed since his death. It was a big deal, financed and organized by the Party. In less than no time, a kind of tent village arose in the park that surrounds the battlements of Castel Sant'Angelo. We had organized various discussions and lectures, inviting poets, politicians, actors, and famous directors. No one had pressured us at all regarding the program or the guests at the debates. I recall among all of them Amelia Rosselli—whom Pasolini discovered—as she was approaching the stage, supported by some vestal of hers, with the air of knowing nothing about either herself or where she was, like a spirit of the underground forced by a spell to walk the earth. Then, however, gaining confidence with the microphone, she began to recite her poems, in that gravelly voice she had, which seemed to move through piles of stone shards—the Pythias must have spoken like that, the ancient Sybils. Just in those September days Italo Calvino died, from a cerebral hemorrhage, leaving unfinished his *Six Memos for the Next Millennium*. Everything went smoothly until the last night. We had decided on a kind of sensational finale, a punch in the stomach to collectively land, an expiatory rite: to show *Salò* on a big outdoor screen in the main piazza. Entrance was free, there was to be no filter of any kind between the work and the people. The version was complete, or at least what was considered complete, and a public showing of this nature had never been done. The trouble was that not even we who had organized the symposium really knew what *Salò* was. When it came out, ten years earlier, we were still children. We should have watched it first, but maybe it was better like this, because the screening, decided on so recklessly, ended up generating a wave of intense emotion, such as rarely happens. People settled on the asphalt of the space as comfortably as they could, forming a sort of enormous encampment. Thousands of beer cans were emptied and crushed without interruption. As at a rock concert, gusts of the heavy sweetish odor of marijuana spread in the warm air. Before the screening began, the white linen of the big screen trembled in the breeze of the late summer evening. In the mid-eighties, the famous 'cultural homogenization' had reached its height. One couldn't imagine a humanity that Pasolini would have hated like that audience. For every sort of reason: from their informal attitude to their way of dressing, from their elaborate carelessness of expression to their obvious bourgeois origins. And yet—a bizarre opposition—*these* were his heirs. The new sub-proletariat no longer knew his name, or the titles of any of his films. Well, he had never been like anyone else, he would not become so after death. Even in his aspect of a ghost, being different stood out, finally, as his supreme quality, the true reason that he had come into the world. And as he was, so was his art, whatever medium he used: a provocation, something that had come to flush you out, disturb you. And that night, during the screening of *Salò*, the mechanism succeeded perfectly. Cinema was still, at that precise historical moment—so far away today that in our eyes it has the light of myth—a force, a magic capable of unleashing itself in the heart, in the guts, in the genitals. It was the burning bush of the Bible, as Andrea Zanzotto once described it.[8] There could be a lengthy discussion on why this force has totally dissipated and was already on the way to dissipation at that time, but that's not my purpose. The fact is that the night of *Salò* Pasolini's genius succeeded in its (typically modern) purpose of putting the patience of its audience to a hard test and finally defeating it, pinning it to an indefinable discomfort, beyond excitement and beyond disgust. In this manner, P.P.P. reached an unprecedented level of psychological involvement, as naturally happens when one is neither flattered nor entertained but, rather, as they say, *wounded to the quick*. Starting from the scene of the forced meal of shit, small groups of people had begun to leave the piazza at Castel Sant'Angelo, without disturbing the others. But the majority stayed, silenced like prey, literally turned to stone. In the pauses in the soundtrack, in that whole crowd one could have heard a mosquito flying. And all this was not in expectation of what, classically, would be called catharsis. There was no release of tension planned, and no purification through the misfortunes of others. The violence of the emotions aroused seemed to remain such, drawing its meaning only from itself. There was no form of *consolation*, in the end, for all that one had been forced to see.

It's very unlikely that, in the bibliographies of Pasolini or in the essays of the most reliable scholars, you will find cited the memoir of one of the leading actors in *Salò*, Uberto Paolo Quintavalle, titled *Giornate di Sodoma* (Days of Sodom) and published in 1976. Quintavalle was a writer, who had met Pasolini, in a completely superficial way, some years earlier. He had no experience, and had been chosen uniquely for his physical appearance, to play a provincial nobleman who knows how to enjoy life. Among the four obscene protagonists of Sade's novel, he embodies Curval, who may be the foulest of them. A sinister and unjust reputation as a vile libel hangs over Quintavalle's work, which is hard to find even in public libraries. A copy in the collection of the Pasolini Foundation at a certain point disappeared into the void, I don't know if by Laura's desire or for some other motive. The fact is that Quintavalle's work was published, less than a year after Pasolini's death, when Pelosi's first trial, a decisive stage of the 'official truth' that was intentionally being constructed, was going on. And some magazine supplement published passages of the book in advance, promising who knows what behind-the-scenes and sexual revelations. In reality, the raciest stories about the film set (it was shot in Mantua in the late winter and spring of 1974) are oral in nature, and in some cases continued to circulate up to our time. Quintavalle's book may be very disappointing from that point of view. There is—it's true—an interesting conversation on dimensions, from which it turns out that for P.P.P. the 'enormous prick' (so important in many key scenes of *Petrolio*) is a myth, a 'nonexistent fantasy.'[9] But on the whole these 'Days of Sodom' are less than sensationalist. In compensation, Quintavalle shows that he possesses two of the most outstanding characteristics of the best portraitists and memoirists: a certain antipathy toward his subject, and a touch of meanness that protects him from the risk of imitation and admiration.[10] For this reason, I consider his book an extremely valuable and truthful document on P.P.P.'s last months, on that movement of metamorphosis-initiation-death engaged without the possibility of second thoughts or backward steps. I feel an analogous effect of truth looking at the photographs of Dino Pedriali—leaving aside the aesthetic disparity.[11] Of course, one can't deny that at times Quintavalle is pointlessly irritating, when his judgments are too superficial. But, like all good gossips, he is endowed with a natural spirit of observation, which allows him to understand that P.P.P. is a man who is exploring in the dark, who has lost his source of pleasure and vital energy and so seeks desperately to raise the stakes. Quintavalle is not the only one to think that the important event marking the start of this extreme phase of research is represented by the marriage of Ninetto Davoli, and it's an acceptable idea provided one considers that marriage, and the resulting separation, a kind of cause of war. The most interesting aspect of this testimony, however, regards not the psychology but the artistic processes, the manner of giving form to these two final experiments, these two catastrophes that are *Salò* and *Petro-lio*. Because the conception, the manner of proceeding, the very intensity of the investment are so analogous, we could almost say that they are a single work, two ways of plumbing the same dark space, the same unspeakable. Let's take, for example, the way he shot the film, personally handling all the takes, carrying the camera on his shoulder, without dollies or other tools. Tonino Delli Colli, his great director of photography, 'prepared the lights and the sets,' Quintavalle recalls, while 'the cameraman studied the focus and lens apertures, then they yielded place to him, and he put his eye to the sight and shot every single meter of the film.' It was a way of working tested long before *Salò*, but in the last film the need to be in the front line, creating with his body 'every single meter of the film,' is dramatically accentuated, with a determination that appears symmetrical with that of the writing of *Petrolio*: telling a story without the filter of a 'narrator,' telling it as an individual 'of flesh and blood,' that is, him, Pasolini. But diving like a dead weight into the final brawl, where the body and its expression can no longer be distinguished from one another,[12] staying in the front line increasingly alone, increasingly unlike his fellows, is only a premise. Then of course there are the things to tell, to recount—the texts, the structure. *Something written.* And in *Salò*, exactly as in *Petrolio*, it's no longer possible to proceed according to a pre-established plan, a line of development. If anything, these are organisms, organs characterized by a *pulse*, they pulse rather than head toward some goal. The possible endings for *Salò* pile up in P.P.P.'s head, just as *Petrolio*, imagined as the posthumous publication of an unpublished text, whose ending is uncertain, accumulates its mysteries without reaching any solution. During a pause on the set of *Salò*, Quintavalle recounts, Pasolini talks to him about this book that he's writing, which has a strange title, *L'armadio* (The Wardrobe), or even *Armadio*, an idea that flashed for an instant and never resurfaced in other documents. Even more interesting is the occasion for the conversation: Quintavalle was talking about an Italian billionaire who had built an empire by exploiting the laws on depressed areas of the country, obtaining for his own use disbursements from the Southern Italy Development Fund. There is no similar character in *Petrolio*, which talks about a different type of powerful person, but P.P.P. would like 'more precise details' about this person. Because it is about a character like this that he intends to speak. Writing *Petrolio* is like digging a hole, big enough so that everything that comes within range will fall into it. And so if P.P.P. happens to hear gossip like this, about the cunning billionaire, he asks for details, because it's precisely such a character that he intends to write about. And when does he intend to start writing about it? At that very moment.[13] But then it's not true, he doesn't intend to talk about anything, not in that sense, what he's doing is something else entirely. And no one understands him.

That the game, which is a real tiebreaker, with no possibility of a rematch, is played on a single table, not exactly 'cinema' and not exactly 'literature,' can also be confirmed by considering everything from another perspective, which is that of rejection of the completed work. When instead—the supreme *realist* intuition—there is nothing that begins and nothing, less than ever, that ends. Everything seethes in its dementia like a primordial serpent, in the light of initiation. Neither cinema, then, nor literature. But this kind of expression and knowledge do not have a name. How could they? At most one could evoke a divinity, or, even better, a disease. But *true* diseases are as many and varied as human beings. Their names would have to coincide with the given names. The Sade novel that P.P.P. follows so *literally*—*The 120 Days of Sodom*—has no end, but after the first part, the only one brought to a relative degree of completion, there is merely a series of increasingly fragmentary notes. Sade transcribed the whole text from earlier notebooks between August and November of 1785, in his cell at the Bastille. The manuscript was a scroll, a *rouleau*, of thin paper made up of pages pasted to one another. After twenty nights of work, on September 12th Sade has completed the first 'side,' and continues on the back. Then, starting on October 22nd, he copies this second 'side,' on thirty-seven more nights of work. We don't know if Sade lost his inspiration or continued to write somewhere else or was satisfied by the work in this incomplete form. The fact is that the night of July 4, 1789, when the Bastille's days are numbered, the Marquis is transferred in haste to the asylum of Charenton. Everything will be lost, his library and, most important, the manuscripts. But, obviously, what shouldn't be lost is never lost, and someone appropriates the *rouleau*, which is passed from hand to hand until 1904, when a psychiatrist named Iwan Bloch published a first, very imperfect edition. It's hard to imagine an interruption more *forced* than this, the prisoner who is transferred from one cell to another, unable to bring his manuscript with him. But isn't this story a perfect allegory of human fate, in its highest degree of truth? Is this not perhaps dying: to be moved from one cell to another, in the middle of a dark night, unable to bring anything with you? The subtlety implicit in the story of Sade's manuscript can't have escaped P.P.P. Precisely because the unfinished manuscript *reeks of life* so intensely it *reeks of death as well.* Pasolini likes this so much that he makes a real mental habit of it. That old nonsense of the found manuscript seems to him the most adequate symbol of everything that's pressing on him. So that *Petrolio*, in the end, has to be presented as 'a critical edition of an unfinished text.' And not too reliable, if you think that of this unfinished text 'four or five versions ... survive: they correspond in some respects and not in others, some contain certain events while others do not.'[14] But it's not enough. In 1975—the year in which P.P.P., remaining faithful to the chilling allegory, ends up *changing his cell* conclusively—Einaudi publishes a text of some years earlier, essentially abandoned out of weariness, that is a kind of rewriting of the Dantesque journey to the beyond, entitled *The Divine Mimesis*. And here he is again, the author of the work given up for dead, while an imprecisely defined 'publisher' reassembles the fragments. This publisher brings out the materials left unfinished by the dead author, which sometimes consist of very short and 'almost illegible' notes, found by chance in the drawers of the dead man, far from the rest of the manuscript, or stuck in books, used as bookmarks. A notepad was found on the dashboard of his car, and, finally, a piece of graph paper ended up in the pocket of the jacket he was wearing at the moment of death. Therefore the 'publisher' protects himself, he *doesn't guarantee* the authenticity of the text, its reliability. As for the author of the work: '*he is dead, beaten to death in Palermo, last year.*' Beaten to death: striking. And that gesture is also enough to evoke the place of the crime, intuitively: it's likely that the corpse of the author of *The Divine Mimesis* was found in some no man's land on the outskirts, a field of parched grass such as there are in Palermo, perfectly identical to those in Rome, in Ostia, everywhere in the world. No space is more ordinary, more universal ... It's the theater of death, the theater of the unfinished.

And then, at a certain point, everything *really* happens, including the details. In 1992, in place of the imaginary editor who posthumously publishes *The Divine Mimesis*, there's a real editor, the great philologist Aurelio Roncaglia,[15] a friend of P.P.P., who, for many years the keeper of a copy of the manuscript, presents to the public the last, unfinished book by Pasolini, in fact 'beaten to death', as the author's note in *The Divine Mimesis* imagined. Finally, the two unfinished things are superimposed, the false and the real. Hypothesized as a fragment of a lost whole, *Petrolio* fulfills that fantasy on the plane of factual reality. It is what it claims to be. A beautiful effect of reality, worthy of a supreme artistic consciousness. But in order for the illusion to be realized—here's the point—it has to explode together with its own bomb. Bring its initiation to an end. Which is not a thing that can be done with the mind, by studying books, relying on the experiences of others. The initiation might include difficult stages, dangerous apprenticeships. All rites of passage are like that: they require submission to certain forms of violence, they anticipate a passage through dark lands, where fear is confronted in solitude. It can be necessary to learn things like: *being a female*, submitting, getting beaten.

Beside the small digression on the two Bosnians protected by Laura, Dragan and Ljuda, the portrait of another persistent visitor to the Pasolini Foundation during this period might be useful here—Walter Siti, who published the complete works of P.P.P., between 1998 and 2003, in ten volumes, achieving what, far from being simply an *edition*, appeared to many a serious *desecration*. So we lacked this as well: usually these complete works are a kind of definitive celebration, an equestrian monument. A slight but insistent ceremonial lunacy presides over their packaging. And instead, poor P.P.P., in this case, too, new scuffles, squabbles, denunciations. Nothing can go in a normal manner with him. He wasn't fated to have, rummaging through his papers, one of those gloomy scholars, as patient and meticulous as terminal illnesses and without any affect, who usually embark on this type of enterprise. And so the restless ghost of P.P.P. finds that his greatest expert, who, as crazy as he is, and charged with erecting the editorial cenotaph, commits instead a crime of *lèse-majesté*, publishing together with the baby all the dirty bathwater. In short, the individual works are inserted into a real flux of drafts, attempts, rewritings. A boiling magma—much more fascinating, in my opinion, than any single piece of solidified lava with its title and its brilliant interpretation. The worshippers of St. Pasolini made these complete works an illness. Personally, I totally agree with Siti. Only disorder interests me, what is unstable and approximate. The methods and processes much more than the so-called results. The equal value of the sketch and the refined product. With these complete works, Siti created a credible image of human life—which is an accumulation of meaningless hypotheses, a trying and retrying, a universal failure with no escape. I was saying that I would like to put Siti in this memoir, but I don't remember him at all in the rooms of the foundation. And he himself reveals the reason for the mystery when I go to see him at his house, many years later, on a chilly spring day in 2011, when I've just begun to write this book and still don't have a clear idea, as always happens to me, what direction to take. Walter did go to the foundation to study, but at night, using the duplicate of a key that Giuseppe Iafrate, the archivist, had gotten for him in absolute secrecy. At a certain point, the Madwoman's rages against him had become too extreme, and Walter had thought it better not to appear during official opening hours. And to think that, at first, it was he who got in touch with Laura, offering to work for her. Shortly before me: *Petrolio* had not yet come out. Walter didn't do it out of masochism: he was in love, and needed to earn some extra money on top of his university stipend. Anyone who has read even one of his books will be able to easily grasp the connection between being in love and the need for money. But with the Madwoman it could only end badly. She always struck your weak spot, says Walter, like an expert fighter. That was, in effect, her weapon. And, obviously, waving P.P.P. in front of the unfortunate's nose, to make him feel like shit—precisely because it was such a crude expedient—was also effective.

Between Walter's house, right off Piazza Risorgimento, and the old home of the Pasolini Foundation, it's only a few hundred meters. You can follow the ramparts of Castel Sant'Angelo, with their enormous diamond points that on winter evenings, extending into the dense fog of the moats, make one think of the claws of a large unidentifiable, pentagonal beast, crouching in the darkness. Benvenuto Cellini managed to escape from there, something that seems impossible, but just at the crucial point he broke a leg. He recounts it in one of the best parts of his memoirs. In the period of imprisonment, he was entrusted to the custody of the chatelain, not a bad man but completely crazy. At unpredictable times, he would start thinking he was a bat. He moved his arms as if they were wings and imitated the shrill cries of bats. When I pass by there, looking at the dark mass of the castle beyond the moats and behind the row of oaks in the park, it occurs to me that the ghost of the mad chatelain might still be hovering around the battlements, convinced that he is the ghost of a bat. Whether infested or not, this neighborhood of Prati, so decorous and professional, crowded by day and half deserted by night, one of the places most densely populated with lawyers and notaries in the world, is the part of Rome that at first glance might make you think least of Pasolini, of the humanity that interested him, of the life that he led. But, especially in Rome, places and people have not always been just as we are used to seeing them. One might say, rather, that, to reach their habitual state and possess it permanently, they have to have passed through, during a long-ago crisis, the exact opposite. Like this neighborhood, which, with its perpendicular intersections, as if it were a small Turin set into the body of Rome, seems to celebrate bourgeois order and the gray prose of daily existence. Because during a certain period it was a very dangerous area, a den of thieves and assassins, prostitutes and abandoned children. And the point is that it was not a neighborhood of hovels and makeshift shelters but the same big buildings of the time of Umberto I that we see today, in different stages of completion. The new neighborhood had begun construction in the last years of the nineteenth century, with a lot of money invested. But then something went wrong, banks failed, and the population of Rome did not grow as expected. Hence the 'Prati di Castello'—the fields of the castle—as it was called, waiting to be redeveloped, had become a dangerous no man's land, to be absolutely avoided at night. Émile Zola, who had a kind of sixth sense for such things, and who in 1894 is in Rome attempting to meet the Pope and to gather information for his new novel, the day after his arrival goes to Prati to take notes and observe people. The words of his diary are as precise as a daguerreotype and as surprising as the description of a dream: 'Vast terrains on which plans for neighborhoods were suddenly created. Chessboard streets, squares. Large, solid houses like barracks. Five stories. Some flat like the façades but in some areas very ornate, with little balusters, balconies, sculptures. Others, simpler, for the poorer people. One sees everything: sites where foundations have been dug then abandoned, sites where the grass has grown again up to the finished, inhabited houses. Houses whose construction was abandoned at the second story, floors open to the sky, windows empty, stone with no facing. Houses with roofs but like empty cages, floors and windows unfinished. Houses finished but shuttered, completely uninhabited. Houses partly inhabited, the rest closed. Finally, houses completely inhabited, proud houses but inhabited by poor people, garbage overflowing from the windows, old clothes hanging from carved balconies, stink and poverty, unkempt women, scantily covered by a dirty shawl, at the windows. All these people barely pay the rent. I'm told that some have even installed themselves in these houses as if by right of conquest. They entered and were left there.' Just so: that Roman plebs is so powerful that it can exercise a kind of 'right of conquest.' There are three great forces that govern it: infantilism, fatalism, an innocent brutality. In his last years, Pasolini had decreed the defeat and the disappearance of that popular world, swept away by consumerism, by bourgeois uniformity. But he had been, exactly as in the celebrated case of the fireflies, too categorical. Precisely because he was a great writer he did *not* possess the supremely journalistic gift of prophecy. More than thirty years later, in Siti's books, everything is again alive and well, perhaps too much so. It's true, the habits and appearances are those of the bourgeoisie, and it's also true that consumerism has become the unique principle of reality and that all reality is merchandise. But this has nothing to do with an extinction and a cultural genocide. If anything, Siti records an astonishing reversal of direction. Now it's no longer the bourgeoisie that is a model for the plebs but the latter that, having absorbed everything there is to absorb, affirms itself as an object of imitation, it's the model for all the bourgeois, it's encamped in the wealthy neighborhoods, just as in Zola's apocalyptic vision. It's a *contagion* that travels on the mercurial wings of speech, of cocaine, of sexual lures.

The door of Walter's house is half open. I find him in the kitchen, dealing with correspondence on his laptop, comforted by an electric heater. He has to go and speak about Pasolini in Milan ('Gratis, obviously') and he wants to make sure that the organizers of the conference at least get him a first class train ticket ('At least that!'). We move to the living room. I had in mind a very specific series of questions about Laura, about P.P.P., about *Petrolio*, but I quickly lose the thread. The people we like and admire induce in us the desire, typically childish, to always hear the same stories. As if, heard yet again, they could still divulge a hidden and revelatory detail, as fables in fact do. Among them, my favorite is the story of Walter, who, at a certain no longer youthful time of his life—as he is crossing that treacherous, foggy no man's land that separates forty from fifty—becomes fed up with academic criticism and starts writing novels. There are beginnings that, in the manner of the ancients, require a sacrifice—and there is Walter, professor of Italian literature at the University of Pisa, who one fine day comes home and throws in the toilet, after reducing it to fragments the size of coriander seeds, an essay on Giacomo Leopardi. And, right afterward, he starts writing his first novel, *Scuola di nudo* (School of the Nude), lying on his stomach like a child with indigestion, as if pouring out his guts were not only one literary metaphor among many but a concrete fact, the assumption of a necessary posture even if uncomfortable and lethal for the back. It's a painstaking job, which should be done a little a day, with an eye on the big sheets of graph paper where he has noted down everything he has to write. He has the sensation of working like the fresco painters of long ago—progressively filling in a space, today a piece of sky, tomorrow the material of a cloak. In spite of certain analogies of content, and all his labor on the complete works, he feels that, as a writer, he has little to do with P.P.P. He knew him only superficially—just at the time when he was starting to write *Petrolio* and setting off toward his end. Walter was very young, studying at the Normale, and, after seeing *Theorem*, overwhelmed by the beauty of Terence Stamp, he decided to write his thesis on *The Ashes of Gramsci*. Then, in view of publication, he had written to Pasolini a couple of times, asking for some clarifications and a meeting. No answer. At that time, Dario Bellizza took care of P.P.P.'s correspondence, and he must have been drowning in similar letters from dozens of students. Walter, in great irritation, had sent a last letter to the poet, telling him to go to hell. And lo and behold P.P.P. had answered, inviting him to visit. He had also offered to publish part of his thesis in *Paragone*. They worked together in P.P.P.'s house on Via Eufrate, in EUR. At the end P.P.P. gave him a ride to the center of Rome. Just as they were saying goodbye, Walter recalls, P.P.P. rested a hand on his thigh, provoking in him a violent and sudden blush. '*Lucky you, still capable of blushing*,' P.P.P. had commented, before disappearing, swallowed up by that city that he knew so well and yet was, and had been for some time, unrecognizable, pervaded and as if corroded by a terrifying alienness.

'*Lucky you, still capable of blushing.*' It seems like a joke, a way of saying goodbye without consequences, and yet the portrait that derives from it, in the light of all that would happen, that was starting to happen, with all the boundaries between the work and the life now collapsed, or, if you like, between saying and doing ... the portrait that derives from it is as reliable as a traffic signal photograph. Where do you go when you're no longer capable of blushing? What have you become and what do you hope? While I'm talking with Walter, the light of a winter afternoon is rapidly transformed into a bluish shadow in which objects, sounds, and finally we ourselves are immersed as in an aquarium. The living room is full of photographs of men who are naked, or covered just enough to obtain an effect even more erotic than nudity itself. In effect, Walter decided to transform his living room into a kind of memorial chapel, dedicated to the ten handsomest men he has gone to bed with. There's only one of whom he still hasn't managed to find an image. 'Starting at fifty,' he tells me, as if thinking aloud, 'I fulfilled my erotic dreams, I lived concretely the fantasies of masturbation, I had what I saw in the magazines. When I think of this fact, it seems to me that I've fulfilled my duty, the reason that I came into the world.' That this joy should be *paid for*, like goods that, the more expensive they are, the more magnificent, exuberant, muscular, not only isn't a problem but is one of the pivots—perhaps the most important—on which all Walter's literature turns. Strange symmetry: just around the age of fifty, reached in 1972, P.P.P. understands that he has lost erotic joy, forever. The reduction of the world to goods seems to him like the inferno that has taken possession of life. In some not precisely definable, and yet evident, way, his transformation into a ghost begins *before* the night of the Idroscalo. *Petrolio* and *Salò* are also this, two bridgeheads, two ways of projecting oneself beyond the confines of one's own life, to adopt the point of view of a dead man. Many aspects of reality that escape the living, as one can easily imagine, are common knowledge for the dead. That makes their perspective particularly interesting. But not infallible. The Achilles' heel of the ghost, if we want to call it that, consists in the fact that, as time passes, the living begin to seem *all the same* to him, like shadows. I say to Walter, to find out what he thinks, that Pasolini's Romanesco, from the first novels, always seemed to me approximate, slightly wooden, with some improbable phonetic details. Walter, who in his books reproduces the language of gyms and the neighborhoods of the periphery with such exactness that one seems to hear it rather than read it, agrees with me. 'He didn't listen, it wasn't his strong point. That wasn't his form of empathy. Maybe he asked a lot of questions, that, yes, as a form ... of affection, of caress. But after Ninetto, I have the idea that he no longer listened to anyone, that all the boys, for him, were absolutely *interchangeable* ... besides it's just like that in Sade's novels ... '

'Death will come and have your *gnocchi*.' It's with this joke that she was very fond of, and which I heard her repeat dozens of times, that the Madwoman erupts in *Troppi paradisi* (Too Many Paradises), Walter's novel published in 2006. It's a literarily superb portrait, with no pointless pity. There is nothing more epidermal, more bound to the surface, than what we call the inner world, the profound I. Like a seagull perched on the highest point of a cliff, the soul is always in the foreground, complete in a pimple, in a slight tic, in the curve of the nose or the tilt of the shoulders. That's why in Walter's book the picture of Laura in the most atrocious years, which were the last, is so believable—when her sick spirit was a body in free fall and at the same time the abyss into which she was falling. Every true catastrophe, then, has an essentially psychosomatic nature. 'Her intelligence is in fact superior to the average of her colleagues,' reflects the protagonist of *Troppi paradisi*, who tries in vain to use Laura's remaining credit for a recommendation for a job at the Rai, the Italian broadcasting system, but 'a lopsided suffering that she brought on herself has devastated her metabolism.' Within the 'Berber tents' of her clothes, the narrator imagines not an organism that has a shape but a collection, a mass of 'individual cellulite lumps,' which wander 'free and fringed.' Something similar to the character in *Star Wars* who has the look of 'a mass of mud spread on the ground, whose mouth opens like an abyss, and whose voice, too, is cavernous.' From this abyss emerge the monologues that had the power to subjugate anyone who was in front of her, thanks to their very foolishness ('Fascism is a very sensual thing, you know, and it doesn't take much to know who is a fascist, I've never made a mistake ... '). The Biological Catastrophe that drags Laura away, in conclusion, seems, if you wish to observe things as they are, less and less like an accident, a misfortune, a disease that might be avoided or cured. On the contrary, according to the protagonist of *Troppi paradisi*, it's the visible manifestation of character, of a 'sadistic and crazy egocentrism' installed at the start in the core of the personality.

Out of the motherless cunt I shall make an obscure, total, obtuse, and absolute soul.

ANTONIN ARTAUD, *Fragmentations*

It's worth repeating: *Petrolio* is a rare beast, a unique specimen. No experiment so risky, dangerous, and in all senses irreversible exists either among the works of P.P.P. or in the literature of his time. Some years ago, thanks to a photocopy, I was able to have the experience of reading the original typescript of this monster work, riddled with corrections and second thoughts. *Petrolio* ought to be reprinted like that, allowing everyone to get an idea of it. Because already the typographical marks, editorial norms, and all the other nagging Lilliputians who afflict the body of the giant only normalize, smooth, control. Usually, what we call a text is a kind of route comparable to a line, more or less straight, which goes from an initial point to another, terminal point. The typescript of *Petrolio* suggests other images. Its movement is not at all linear: if anything, it evokes the spiral circularity of a whirlpool, like a liquid sucked into a hole. It wouldn't be inapt to think of the water in the toilet, at the moment when you pull the chain. We mustn't ever forget, in fact, that *Petrolio* is not another book about death but a *death in progress*. No initiation can get around the necessity of death. In order to approach the supreme vision, in the terminal light of the reality that he has finally won, the man will have to get rid of himself, leaving behind his old identity, like the dried up shell of the cicada. To avoid misunderstandings, P.P.P. indicates what he is talking about in a really pedantic manner, scattering in the text precise, unmistakable signs. And yet little of this undertaking—so original, so skillfully transforming *something written* into the supreme experience of life, far beyond the very concept of 'literature'—has been understood by his few readers. When it appeared in the bookstores, *Petrolio* caused a sensation for some very racy sex sequences, in particular the notorious Note 55, *The field beside Via Casilina*, in which Carlo the Second, transformed into a woman, is possessed in various positions by twenty boys paid for the purpose. But the best was yet to come. Based on the novels' chapters devoted to the career of Carlo within Eni, various revelations have been attributed to Pasolini's work, concerning sordid Italian crimes of the financial-political type. It has to be said that, judging from what remains to us of *Petrolio*, P.P.P. is a very incompetent and lazy investigator. His greatest intellectual effort seems to have been that of having a friend send him a photocopy of a hard-to-find book about the financier Eugenio Cefis. For the rest, as has been documented with precision,[16] P.P.P. copied entire passages of articles he read in *L'Espresso* and elsewhere. But everyone knows that the 'mystery,' the noir, the intrigue with death are temptations too strong to be mined effectively by common sense. The average Italian character, if one can put it like this, feels *ennobled* by any form of investigation, legal case, inquiry into crimes and those responsible. Above all the literati of the left (which is equivalent to saying the overwhelming majority of literati) honor, in the detective, the supreme form of knowledge and, in a sense, the quintessence of human nobility. They by far prefer Mickey Mouse, just to be clear, to the lazy Donald Duck. And so how to resist the temptation to read *Petrolio* as the trail, the monstrous index of truths so burning as to cost the author his life? All the more since *Petrolio*, by its fragmentary nature, lends itself to this much more than any finished text. Because if what we read is disappointing, a great deal might have been removed, with criminal surgery, by someone sneaking at night into the house of the writer.[17] Oddly, what has not been noted is that, based on such deductions, the image of P.P.P. that would emerge from a book so dense with dangerous revelations about Eni would resemble that of a vulgar blackmailer, a spy, an informer with his fingers in many pies. Individuals of this type existed by the dozen, in the Rome of the seventies. Journalists with connections in the secret services, spongers at receptions, shady types specializing in blackmail, artists of the hint and the double cross. Depending on circumstances, and the ability to place a limit on one's own claims—the most difficult of human abilities—they could end up with a bullet in the head or at the highest levels of some government ministry, or in parliament. Say what you like about P.P.P., but he would not have been able to imitate, even jokingly, that scum. 'I don't have the evidence,' he said—and it was true. And his target was so high that it was at risk of ending up, in the eyes of others if not in fact his own, completely invisible.[18]

That target, the supreme and conclusive subject of the discourse, consists, we can say, in a radical and irreversible transformation of the whole being, which is manifested in the form of a *vision*, or a progressive series of visions. All in all, despite its completely chaotic appearance, it's possible to attempt a synthesis, a panorama, of *Petrolio*, if not a real summary. It's the account of an initiation—twofold because, as we've said many times, the hero of the 'poem' (as Pasolini himself called it) is double. The story begins on a May morning in 1960, with the doubling of the hero, Carlo Valletti, a young petroleum engineer (he was born in Alessandria in 1932) who got his degree in Bologna in 1956, a Catholic of the left, destined to a brilliant career at Eni. Carlo's double (Carlo the Second, or Karl, as Pasolini thinks of calling him in an early phase) is instead a humble person, 'untouched and uncontaminated.' Like all the humble, 'without social authority,' he is 'good.' And it is in an atmosphere of absolute and perfect innocence that all his extraordinary erotic adventures take place, while the 'first' Carlo, the engineer, is condemned by birth and education to guilt, to doubt, to awareness. As soon as the doubling happens, the two Carlos separate. On a page of notes written in Beirut, May 5, 1974, P.P.P. jotted down a general outline for the travels of the two

Carlos. Carlo the First goes to the Middle East, to the places where Eni began to invest billions in petroleum research. Two more trips to the East will follow, having to do with a mystical conversion—in fact a kind of 'fall in Damascus.' But of this plot development only a few traces remain. Carlo the Second, on the other hand, spied on by a mysterious Pasquale on the orders of powerful and even more mysterious persons, leaves for Turin right after the doubling, for the apparent purpose of spending some days with his family, going to the places where he grew up, seeing old friends, etc. And instead, in the period spent in Turin, as a *Balance Sheet* will reveal, 'Carlo had complete sexual relations—and for the most part repeatedly—with his mother, with his four sisters, with his grandmother, with a friend of the last, with the family servant, with her fourteen-year-old daughter, with two dozen girls of the same age and even younger, with a dozen women in his mother's "set." '

In *Troppi paradisi* Siti did not exaggerate at all, out of a love for the grotesque or the sensational. Laura's physical and mental conditions worsened from day to day, as in those horror films in which a terrifying and unstoppable metamorphosis takes place—like Cronenberg's *The Fly*. She made life unbearable for others, but it was what she did to herself that was most striking. She wasn't yet seventy, but years earlier her age and her appearance had taken two different paths. A decline won't be the happiest thing in life, but that, too, one would say, you have to deserve. Laura didn't even imagine what a decline was. Hers was a perpendicular collapse, a fall like a dead weight, where the velocity increases meter by meter. No pause, no remedy. Certain health precautions taken by people her age enraged her ('Pressure!! *Cho-les-ter-ol!!!* What, they don't want to die? You get it, little slut? THE MORE USELESS YOUR LIFE IS THE LESS YOU WANT TO DIE!!!') She smoked, ate, shouted. She shouted, ate, smoked. The food she swallowed was of a worse quality. She boasted of being a great cook, and in fact, when she had guests, she went to some trouble. But bulimia and the need to get bad food quickly, to gorge on, go together. She began to love takeout Chinese, and those frozen foods where each item looks like a little cube, and thaws in the pan. Five minutes, three minutes: it was the faster time that attracted her, not the type of product. In the bathroom of the foundation she had set up a gas stove and some big pans, and with this rudimentary equipment she coped with attacks in the office. One of the secretaries had told me that, to avoid at least the nighttime bulimia, she had put a lock on the kitchen door, and every night, after dinner, she gave the key to the porter in her building. Alas, it wasn't a normal door but two wood panels hinged to the doorpost, one of those saloon doors you see in Westerns. There was no way that Laura could even think of climbing over it, but the space between the bottom and the floor, in this type of door, is wide enough to try to crawl under. And here is the Madwoman who, in the middle of the night, tries to get to the fridge … and remains stuck there on the floor, exhausted and furious, until the maid comes to her aid. Our mind should construct walls of modesty, should compel us not to imagine people in situations so humiliating, so painful, that they are intolerable even for the stranger who happens by. But are we really sure that compassion is the most elevated sentiment? I think something much superior exists: recognition of the full humanity a person can reach. This fullness is never precisely definable, but one thing is certain: it's pointless to look for it it in noble postures, in dignity, in harmony of gestures. The tenacious worm of the ridiculous corrodes all monuments, until a breath is enough to reduce them to dust. Full humanity, on the contrary, isn't the product of either euphemism or censorship. Its principal ingredients are suffering and comedy, so mixed up and confused that it's impossible to distinguish them. Unique among all the forms of known life, our life, if we consider it

for what it is, arouses laughter and tears simultaneously—
and it's not easy to clearly identify the motivations for either
one. And the image of that enormous woman, desperate,
starving, trapped in the doorway of her kitchen, seems to
me, as I think back on it, to shine with an internal light, and
a kind of metaphysical certainty—the only one possible. It's
a punishment so big that it contains in itself, preserved in its
very abjectness, its redemption.

Dragan and Ljuda had introduced me to a friend of theirs, Maria, who lived in their building in Trastevere. They had met her by chance at the supermarket, and within a few minutes had discovered they had the same tastes, the same fetishes. Chains, whips, rituals of submission. It was early March, 1994: I remember it well because the first evening the four of us spent together, in the elegant pied-à-terre belonging to Laura's friend, which the two Bosnians had transformed into a kind of dump, we talked a lot about Kurt Cobain, who was in Rome on vacation, but from the Excelsior, on Via Veneto, he had gone to the hospital, because of an overdose of champagne and Rohypnol. He would shoot himself in the face a few weeks later, having returned to Seattle, leaving a long and moving farewell letter (*'Peace, love, empathy'*). That, too, was a sign: the twentieth century was really ending: there would still be rock music afterward, of course, but never again anything like Nirvana, just as already there had been nothing like the paintings of Pollock or the books of Pasolini or Artaud or Mishima. Only the interpreters remained, the unhappy heirs, bent under the weight of obsolete riches, which they would never be able to spend. With the proofs of my first book ready, there was little to laugh at: it's better not to be invited to the party at all, rather than arrive when everyone is leaving.

Like Ljuda, Maria was a true slave. Sex, for her, had always been an accompaniment to really strong dishes: suffering, humiliation, dependency. Above all, she loved the perfection of the rituals with the same passion as a Byzantine liturgist, or a master of ceremonies in an imperial Chinese court. Because in sadomasochism ritual is, in a certain sense, everything, and ultimately coincides with the thing itself. One who makes a mistake is lost, immediately marginalized. The only heir of a very wealthy Palermitan family, the daughter of a famous Mafia lawyer, refined and witty, even if not excessively intelligent, elegant, and thin as a rail, Maria had all the qualities to be considered, in certain Roman brotherhoods, a true authority. When she was still very young, a German had initiated her into the pleasures of branding, or of being *marked*, like a docile cow. This man, it seems, was a true spiritual guide, and could count on the devotion of a harem of dozens of slaves. For him, Maria had abandoned her architecture studies (pursued without much enthusiasm) and moved to Berlin, where she had learned everything she could learn. At a certain point, she had become fed up with the Master, and now she was settled in Rome, with her expensive clothes and her flamingo-like beauty. I couldn't understand why Dragan and Ljuda had been so eager for me to meet Maria. If only because of my sloppiness in dress and appearance, intolerable to sadomasochistic eyes, you could see from a mile away that I was completely insensitive to the fascination of rituals and suffering, whether inflicted or endured. The first time I heard talk about branding, I had pretended to understand, as I often do when I don't feel like asking for explanations, but I thought it had something to do with brandy. Maybe the Bosnians thought that within me slept a slave, or a master, waiting to awaken at the right moment. Or they thought that Maria, all things considered, could be comfortable with a person not involved with her predominant passion. It doesn't have to be your boyfriend who whips you, or licks the soles of your shoes. The fact is that things between Maria and me didn't go badly, at first. I've always found lightness very attractive, in women, especially joined to a degree of obtuseness, if not pure and simple stupidity. Maria, besides, had that benevolent curiosity about the doings of her fellow-man—a pleasant mixture of interest, irony, and indifference—which only people who don't do a damn thing from morning to night have, and can afford to.[19] So she had begun to read the material on Pasolini and Sade that I had obtained for Dragan and Ljuda on Laura's orders, and that for months had been lying untouched among their things, part in the kitchen, part next to the bed. Surprisingly, Sade didn't interest her: too much sex for her taste. Sade's libertines, she explained to me, always ended up coming, even if amid great difficulties, with the sperm reduced to a few blackish drops. But sexual excitement wasn't the center of the affair: the paradox consists in the fact that Sade himself fell into that beginners' mistake. Sadomasochistic philosophy involves a series of initiations, an advance toward the essential in an increasingly rarefied, frozen mental atmosphere. According to Maria, compared with Pasolini Sade was a kid. Both in *Salò* and in *Petrolio*, he had aimed directly at the center of the target. And in fact they were two absolutely *chaste* works—that was the word Maria used.[20] Probably, he was fed up with sex, but she didn't know enough about the work or the man to understand when or how. That doesn't mean that P.P.P. had planned to go to bed early or, even worse, have a steady boyfriend. No, he would continue to seek young flesh every night, to the end, cost what it might cost. But sex, by now, was like a door, an entrance to an ecstasy of a different nature. If one knew how to read it with attention, and with the right degree of empathy, *Petrolio* was a document that could be trusted. Maria had requisitioned from Dragan and Ljuda a copy of the book that was drifting uselessly among their stuff, and had plunged into reading it. She didn't share my admiration: it seemed to her she had read a pile of disjointed and contradictory notes. But some pages had struck her so forcefully that she copied them diligently into a notebook. In Maria's opinion, everything that Pasolini was writing in the last years was the product of a discovery that had to do with himself, not the external world. And it was a secret so great, the light it contained was so dazzling, that the words were in danger of not standing up to the collision, of turning out to be caskets too fragile for that so long repressed energy. But one thing was certain: *Petrolio* could have been written only by someone who had fully understood the hypnotic fascination of violence, the desire to submit, to be subjugated, to beg for mercy hoping that that mercy, up to and beyond the limits of the tolerable, would be denied.

In *Petrolio* there is an abundance of dead wood or, if you prefer, interrupted paths. Branches that are not developed, and remain there, fragments without a future, stubs of plot. This fact can cause some confusion. What is *Petrolio* about, in the end? One mustn't lose sight of the principal. After following Carlo the Second to Turin, and having described minutely his embarrassing return to the family, the book concentrates on Carlo 'par excellence (in the sense of social privilege).' For this character, too, much less likable than the first, consumed by a desire for power that is like an incurable sickness, with his myopic gaze and sagging flesh, destiny has reserved experiences that are to say the least exceptional. For now, the story shows him in Rome, on an elegant street in the Parioli, while he prepares to attend a reception at the house of 'Signora F.' This salon of Signora F., with its collection of seventeenth century painters, is one of those places teeming with journalists, politicians, operators, and spies weaving their grim destinies. There is nothing more repugnant, in Pasolini's eyes, than this sort of place, typically Roman, where power guarantees for itself, in an atmosphere of ironic conviviality, longevity. But it is precisely that through which Carlo has to pass, in his advance toward the top of the pyramid. And P.P.P. takes advantage of it to insert into the story a long digression on the very powerful Aldo Troya and his financial empire. As we know, Aldo Troya is a name invented by Pasolini, but the portrait corresponds plainly to that of Eugenio Cefis—a man in fact powerful and dangerous, at the center of a vast network of relations between politics, financial affairs, and the secret services. But the whole stink of 'truth,' so to speak, that invades this part of the book is an *effect of art*, and does not derive in the least from any firsthand information. The truth is that P.P.P. copies everything he writes in *Petrolio* about Cefis/Troya from another book, *Questo è Cefis* (This Is Cefis), by Giorgio Steinmetz, limiting himself to some harmless variations. The story of this short book, whose full title is *Questo è Cefis: L'altra faccia dell'onorato presidente* (This Is Cefis. The Other Face of the Honored President), is very interesting.[21] It was published in 1972 by AMI, or Agenzia Milano Informazioni. Despite the name, this agency could exist only in Rome, picking up the gossip of the most sordid parliamentary undergrowth. AMI's owner and man of all work, besides the only contributor, was a journalist, Corrado Ragozzino, who should be played by Alberto Sordi. *Questo è Cefis* is a book implicated in some obscure power struggles. And it rapidly became a bibliographic ghost, impossible to find even in the major public libraries. But it wasn't a large number of readers that the author aspired to. The book was a challenge, a sort of trial of power, of threat addressed directly to Cefis and his loyalists. It has been said and repeated, without verification, that the book was actually written by Corrado Ragozzino, its publisher. More convincing is the hypothetical portrait of the author of *Questo è Cefis*, painted by Corrado's nephew, Guglielmo

Ragozzino, also a journalist, in a 2005 article devoted to the whole affair: 'Very likely he was a minor character, deep inside Eni, and slightly connected to the secret services, who had access to some archives and wanted to keep Cefis under watch, maybe on behalf of someone, in politics and in business.' It's a human profile worth reflecting on. In the eternal Italian commedia dell'arte, with its trite customs and its well-known witticisms, the role of the dull scribe who preserves his dossiers, half true half false, always boasting about some debt—in a word, of the shrewd *operator*, is an eternal, unchangeable mask. Now, the relationship between the author of *Petrolio* and the author of *Questo è Cefis* is a grand satirical invention. Because P.P.P., purposely, imitates the anonymous operator. He pretends to take the point of view of the dung heap. But he does it because he is seeking, supreme writer that he is, a particular artistic effect. About Eni itself, about the death of Enrico Mattei, about the career of Eugenio Cefis Pasolini cares absolutely nothing at all. *'I am able to do all this,'* he confesses at a certain point, *'only on the condition that I take it as a game, as entertaining as possible.'*

In any case, it's in the loathsome salon of Signora F. that the career of Carlo Valletti makes a leap forward. It's a question of accepting, from Eni ('anything but a simple company'), a job that involves a trip to the East. It's an apparently bureaucratic job, but at a deeper level it takes shape as a real rite of passage—'a trip to the East isn't an everyday occurrence,' seeing that its authentic meaning always resides 'in myth.' And Pasolini intends to make this first trip of his hero to the East, to the places where Eni (we're in the early sixties) is spending billions on petroleum research, conform to the model of a mythical journey, that of the Argonauts in search of the Golden Fleece, as recounted by Apollonius of Rhodes. This part of *Petrolio* was to be deliberately unreadable, because it was to be written in modern Greek. Pasolini confines himself to writing (in Italian) some careful summaries of it, similar to those which used to appear at the start of the chapters in works of a certain length. Even in these summaries the theme of the journey as initiation returns insistently. '*The true birth is the second birth*,' we read at a certain point.

On the other hand, the job of the trip to the East accepted by Carlo isn't the only aspect of the evening at Signora F.'s salon that alludes to a ritual, an initiation. Despite its incompleteness, *Petrolio* is a work that is extraordinarily consistent in its intentions and, so to speak, its basic convictions. Thus, throughout the work, the idea of *mystery* and the idea of *story* are joined to the idea of *power*. One might say that this sort of threatening trinity is the still completely unrecognized pinnacle of Pasolini's political and philosophical thought. Where there is power, in fact, there is mystery, but both mystery and power, if one wants to talk about them, or even if they are to emerge, have to assume the guise of a story. In the story, understood as mystery, it's always power that is made evident. As, farther on, we will see happening at the Quirinal, no less, during the reception for the Festival of the Republic, so in Signora F.'s salon a circle of narrators appears, as if under a spell, isolated from the worldly noise that surrounds them. As if they were officiating at a rite, these narrators exchange stories—*cultivated accounts*, Pasolini defines them in a note. It's certainly not a coincidence that the first of these stories is entitled *First fable on Power*. Two others follow: *The purchase of a Slave* and *The story of the city of Patna and the region of Bihar*. The situation could change: from the salon of Signora F. to a vaguely defined 'intellectual gathering,' modeled on analogous scenes in *The Brothers Karamazov*. A story is a mystery, according to this bold and solitary conception of Pasolini's, not because it contains secrets or enigmas but because in it, through it, the nature of power becomes evident. Therefore, of necessity, the power that lurks in the stories is immense, even when they like to take on the appearance of an innocuous worldly entertainment. Undoubtedly, says one of the narrator guests at Signora F.'s salon, telling stories is a pleasure. But this pleasure 'always sins by excess.' One always decides to tell 'something,' in fact: choosing one subject instead of all the others. But this choice is completely illusory—it hides the totality without removing it. 'Anyone who decides to tell a story,' in fact, 'immediately has the possibility of describing the entire universe.'

(There is also, in the course of this story, a few lines after such a demanding statement, a supreme touch of humor, worthy of the intelligence of P.P.P.—'*Anyone who speaks to you there,*' the narrator reminds his listeners, '*is a journalist.*')

I remember well the last evening I spent at Laura's house in the big gloomy old palazzo on Via di Montoro. I'm even sure of the date, March 28, 1994, because it was the day of Berlusconi's first electoral victory, and Laura had invited some people to come and watch the results together, dusting off for the occasion her talents as a cook. There is nothing more *Roman*, in the most sinister and melancholy meaning of the term, than the palazzo where Laura lived, blackened by time long before the fumes of the traffic arrived to do their part.[22] You have to have spent a lot of time observing these buildings, which always seem to display a kind of desperate solemnity, to begin to understand their true purpose and their true nature. Only in appearance are the old palazzos of Rome made to be inhabited. It's true that people spend their lives there, love, die, as elsewhere. But then you have merely to walk in these grim baroque neighborhoods on a winter evening, when there's no sound but the rain falling, and no people around ... and those big buildings will emerge as what they are: doors, sumptuous trapdoors to the Lower World. You have only to slip into a half-open doorway to get an idea. In the shadowy light of the entrance, you make out the row of mailboxes, the elevator door, the first flight of steps. But there is always, even if you don't notice, a small dilapidated door, secured by a padlock. If you were allowed to open that door, you would find another stairway, much narrower and darker than the one that leads to the upper floors. Nothing odd: it's the entrance to the cellars, dug out of the foundations. No one can deny it: these cellars, deep as they are, are only the upper level of a subterranean world without end—well, funnel, labyrinth of eternal shadows. Gradually, as one descends, catacombs, tunnels, storerooms, and crypts give way to immense caves, often occupied by lakes, cold, shapeless expanses of water that have never known living beings—except perhaps some rat that's lost its way, and comes to die exhausted on the sharp stone edge. And farther down? Who could ever imagine the forms of Nothingness, which are innumerable and at the same time all similar to a single, immense shadow? From down there, from that tangle of darkness and privation, rise miasmas so powerful that they reach the world of the living, so subtle and insidious that they penetrate walls, seep into fabrics, spread an invisible film on food, on plants, on materials. In the old palazzos of Rome, one always hears some inexplicable sound, there is always some macabre gossip that is handed down among the tenants, while the domestic animals, able to see and hear things that have been hidden from us since childhood, spend their life in long wars against unimaginable, unnamable enemies. Almost everyone who lives in the center of Rome, and especially in the immense aristocratic palaces transformed into condominiums, is at least slightly disturbed, unstable in mood, often daydreaming. And then there are people like Laura, whose soul seemed made of the same impenetrable night from which—with unforgivable recklessness—the houses, the streets, the squares with their fountains are constructed. The apartment on Via di Montoro was nicely furnished: maybe, as time passed, her taste had become more sober compared with the mad years of Via del Babuino. It can't be said that Laura, at least in theory, disliked having guests. She knew, it can be said, all the artists, directors, writers, actors of her generation. It was a real world, a small social universe in which all the elements, even the most dissimilar, were bound by the same feeling of belonging. Laura was part of it in a permanent, indisputable way, as by virtue of a birthright. And if in every form of madness a strong component of solitude and isolation is implicit, well, the paradox embodied in Laura is that the solitude of madness did not necessarily exclude sociability, as she saw people every night of her life, in a perpetual exchange of invitations, appointments, small daily bits of news, telephone gossip. In that context, Laura's impossible character was a feature polished by habit like all others, like being homosexual, being rich, being fat, being hypocritical, being good. Certainly the dinners at her house became less frequent after the death of Moravia, who ordered the menu by telephone, sending her to buy fish at the Campo dei Fiori market and drawing up the list of guests to invite. But never ever would Laura have watched the election results on television without being able to talk to someone, without hearing what a good assortment of her peers had to say about them. You can't invite an entire society to your house: so in every living room, around every table, a reliable miniature is reproduced, a metonymy. And that evening Laura had chosen, between husbands and wives, maybe ten or so people—all drawn with assurance from the old crowd. But that evening, so ordinary that it could be confused with dozens and hundreds of others, was also, simultaneously, Berlusconi's evening. That disgusting Milanese, who was the incarnation of everything that Laura's world despised and abhorred, for emotional and psychological reasons even more than political, had made it, had leaped into the saddle. They wanted him in jail, they wanted him dead, and here he was, in command. As the first results appeared on the TV screen, on that warm windy evening in late March, expressions grew melancholy, conversation languished, a suspect and unusual wish to return home made its way among those present. All that endowed the dinner with a bizarre, contradictory two-part nature, because on the one hand it was a dinner like many others, with the people and the conversations that you would have expected, and on the other something was happening: the most unpleasant of exterminating angels had come in through the window and promised nothing good. I remember, as if it were an emblem, Stefano Rodotà, who got up from the table and, alone in the middle of the room, with his hands behind his back, skillfully practiced a dribbling exercise, using a crumpled piece of paper that he bounced on his polished moccasin, his figure impeccable even in that childish activity. Next to me Enzo Siciliano, who at the time was preparing the second edition of his *Pasolini:A Biography*, literally groaned every time there was an update of the results on the TV screen. Francesca Sanvitale, instead, seemed more afflicted by the bad mood of her friends than by the political disaster itself. The trouble wasn't only him, Berlusconi. If the state of mind of those people was gloomier than that usually inspired by election results, assuming the heavy features of depression, similar to those of victims of a personal insult, if in short it couldn't have been worse for them, the reason is that the Party, this time, had made a huge mistake. The imbeciles who led it had been sure of winning hands down. And in order not to give them the satisfaction, the people—the dull and stupid people—had voted for the Monster of Milan. And now here he was: double-breasted suit, shoes with the lift in the heel, and that incredible polka-dot tie. In some measure, all Laura's guests might have harbored, toward the Communist Party, or what it was called later, feelings of detachment, and even revulsion. But basically they had never doubted that that immense institution, that human pyramid with its ill-considered mass, *was useful for something*. If not to fulfill happiness on this earth, which only fools consider possible, at least to protect them from the fact that someone like *that* should carry home first prize. Well? The Party, on that crucial occasion, had been good for nothing. All that could be hoped, now, was that the repercussions of the disaster on individual lives would be as light as possible. But there was little to be happy about. As for him, P.P.P., the old ghost was the only one who had never had illusions about the Party. Hadn't it expelled him like someone with the plague at the first scandal? Hadn't the Party always been, on certain matters, more hypocritical and bigoted than the priests themselves? But, above all, to say Party meant saying power, and power is always an evil, there is no power without evil. And what did they want, those old friends, Enzo Siciliano and all the others—what had they expected? P.P.P. smiled, good-humored, from behind the thick lenses of his glasses, at his ease in that living room where he had spent so many evenings when he was alive. When I felt the presence of the ghost, I always clothed him, in imagination, in the blue jean shirt of the photographs of Dino Pedriali taken a few days before his death. Skinny, concentrated, intense. He, too, had decided to spend that evening in company, and had settled in the corner of one of the sofas, far from the table, because he had no need to eat. In a few minutes, the Milanese would come out of his den, to speak on television, the crown on his head. P.P.P. had not predicted him, that one can't say and it's not in any work. It was impossible for him, *physiologically* impossible, to conceive of a man like Silvio Berlusconi. If for some work of his he needed to describe people of that stuff, as in *Petrolio*, he copied from newspaper articles. He couldn't *know them.* As the hours of that sad evening passed, and the tables with their columns of figures succeeded one another on the screen, as in a demented version of Lotto, in the farthest corner of Laura's living room the ghost of P.P.P., arms folded and chest tilted forward, was roaring with laughter, he laughed with the abandon of someone who doesn't even know himself what he's laughing about. A ghost, by its nature, acts unobserved—if not completely, almost. Instead, at the peak of the dismay, with the projections of the results now solidly headed for defeat, Laura took care of providing an interesting distraction for her guests. She let out a kind of groan, a light roar, one might say, and then collapsed on some unfortunate person—I think I remember that it was Mario Missiroli. Like a tribe of Eskimo fishermen, who get busy around the mass of the just captured sperm whale to haul it onshore, we all worked to deposit Laura on her bed, leaving to the ladies the job of comforting her. Offers came to stay and sleep there. But Laura didn't want to know about it. Now she felt fine. It was just the shock. Berlusconi and existence. Berlusconi as *symbol* of the life that was left to live. Now we could all go. The evening was over. He, P.P.P., would keep watch at the bedside of his friend. Convincing at least her (the others could never get to that point) that, all things considered, even this was a splendid occasion for laughter. Maybe there would even be time for a pleasant spin in the car. He was used to going to bed late.

As in the best classic novels, in *Petrolio*, too, long periods of time can be condensed into a single sentence. For a good ten years, the relations between the engineer Carlo Valletti and his double, Carlo the Second, or Karl, go forward in an idyllic manner, and there is little to tell. The doubling has produced a habit not without sweetness. Like two old spouses who no longer have a lot to say to one another but know that this is the surest evidence of their happiness, the two Carlos spend the first part of the evening together, and then plunge into their respective destinies. For Carlo the Second, night brings the period of greatest activity. For the engineer, on the other hand, it's time to go to bed. But this tranquility, obviously, can't last. We are in fact nearing a catastrophe, or the *First fundamental moment of the poem*. So that the work can proceed toward its goal, burning its very premises in its surprising development, from the initial metamorphosis a new metamorphosis has to arise, even more crucial than the first, considered from the point of view of the knowledge that it will produce. This new metamorphosis will also be double, affecting both Carlos, one after the other, and will be reversible, because at a certain moment both will return to their original condition. These events punctuate the book, creating a symmetry of 'fundamental moments.' It's Carlo the Second who becomes a woman first.

'Two large breasts—no longer young—hung from his chest; and below his belly there was nothing: the hair between his legs had disappeared and—only by touching it and pulling apart the lips—did Carlo, with the clear gaze of one who from his experience as an outlaw has learned the philosophy of the poor, see the little wound that was his new sex.'

'At this point, reader, the poem takes off.' Just like that: like the great artist he could be, P.P.P. keeps his promise. And Note 55 of *Petrolio*, entitled *The field beside Via Casilina*, is one of those results that are rarely achieved in the life of a writer. Like the spires of Gothic churches. When *Petrolio* came out, in 1992, much of the scandal was focused on these pages. But if many among even the most illustrious and qualified readers hadn't understood that it wasn't a scene of homosexual sex—imagine the rest. Having become a woman, Carlo immediately wants to experience this new condition. After some uncertainty, she begins to think in a big way, as is Carlo's nature when it comes to sex. No sooner said than done: she pays twenty youths, who will possess her in turn in a big field in the neighborhood of Via Casilina, at the southern edge of Rome—one of those no man's lands that emerged, even in the early seventies, in the areas already invaded by the new neighborhoods, waiting for the new waves of building speculators. No need to say that here, too, in this poor, dusty setting, there is an obvious whiff of the Idroscalo, of the last stop. It's night—'The whole cosmos was there, in that field, in that sky, in those barely visible urban horizons, and in that intoxicating odor of summer grass.' It's the poignant and solemn atmosphere most propitious for a leap forward, the first mutation. The twenty boys await their turn forming a noisy group of shadows, while Carlo waits for them meekly, on her knees, a little apart, as is fitting for a sacrificial beast. With the arrival of the first youth, all the sacred that had spread through the night, saturating it to the distant horizon of houses on the periphery, is concentrated in a single point. '*The cock always appeared in the form of a miracle.*' Carlo, as the hours of the sacred night follow one another, burns in the ecstasy of submission. In her slightest gesture or attitude as a 'good whore,' a new, irreversible knowledge shines.

The penis: '*the sole reality.*'

I repeat: these pages of *Petrolio* are a masterpiece of the art of Italian prose. To understand the level of refinement of the enterprise, we need only focus on a detail, in a brief digression that we might call *Adventures of the Glans*. If the penis is 'the sole reality,' what to say of its head, its tip? But there is something strange that may seem incomprehensible. At the moment of sending the first edition of *Petrolio* to be typeset, in 1992, Aurelio Roncaglia warned readers about it in a brief note entitled *A Curiosity*. The glans, that is 'the front part of the male member,' appears in *Petrolio* as if it were a feminine noun. '*La glande rosea, lucida e asciutta* (the rosy, shiny, and dry glans),' for example. According to Roncaglia, by doing so Pasolini would retrieve that 'acorn' (*ghianda*) which inspired, metaphorically, the anatomical term.[23] All right: but why did he do it? Roncaglia's philological explanation reveals no motive for such a glaring infraction of the rule. We also have to consider the fact that, a couple of times, Pasolini uses the term normally, in the masculine: *il glande*. But above all we have to consider that the linguistic strangeness surfaces in the text in proximity to the change of sex and the sexual initiation of the two Carlos when they become females. The other Carlo, the engineer, will also find two breasts on his chest and a crack between his legs, and will proceed rapidly to an encounter with 'the sole reality.' In this new episode, we'll see, there is only one penis, but it's even more powerful and numinous, if possible, than those of the twenty boys. And it's here that we read a revelatory sentence, within which, and in a completely intentional way, in my view, *il glande* and *la glande* coexist peacefully. 'He opened his mouth and the enormous tip [and so far it can be both masculine and feminine] went in: it [masculine] was perfumed, it had the taste of an infant and not only the tip [feminine!] but the skin below, darkly brown, seemed of silk.' In other words it's not that Pasolini mistakes the gender of a word, or purposely uses the wrong one, but he invents an oscillation that doesn't exist. He is celebrating sexual mutation and androgyny as the key for entrance to a further and definitive level of reality, and just at the point of maximum irradiating energy, at the tip of the penis, he wants both, male and female, *il glande* and *la glande*, with that same confusion, like a faint reddening of the tongue, because of which in Italian one says both *il clitoride* and *la clitoride*. And with this very light brushstroke, with this microscopic mystification, everything that's possible to think about that 'sole reality' becomes complicated, expands, becomes infinitely richer and seductive and damp and dangerous ...

One morning when I was working on the P.P.P. interviews the Madwoman erupted into the reading room waving a copy of the *Corriere della Sera*. A review had come out of my first book, just published, and it had sparked the most unrestrained sarcasm. 'And so our little slut has become *FAMOUS*!!! ... well, well ... that's what you always wanted, right? To enter the Elect Band of Shits ... *of those who've made it*!!! And what could be better, for our little slut, than to write books? She writes in the morning ... and in the evening she's pleased as Punch. SHE LAUGHS!!!' Even if I made the effort to listen to her as if she were a person making normal conversation, I never understood anything the Madwoman was saying. Even when I've quoted bits of her ravings, in quotation marks, it's just to give a pale idea, a reflection of that uncontrollable magma. And yet every so often, just because it was incomprehensible, some phrase seemed to hit the mark, to uncover some lie. Write in the morning and be pleased as Punch at night ... how horrible! The Madwoman was right. P.P.P. didn't behave like that. *He didn't act pleased as Punch.* Instantaneous and irrefutable as the design of a Zen master, that little man who writes and then *laughs* was the perfect portrait of what I had always abhorred. The cultured Italian and his underground joys, like a petty demon. It's really true that the Madwoman had a talent for seizing on weak points, so weak that not even her victims knew they had them. By now my stay at the Pasolini Foundation was coming to an end. Those interviews had to be published, to be eligible for some public funding, and one of these days I had to show Laura the plan for the work. I knew there would be anything but laughter, in that case, and that the game would end there. But we had put off everything until after a trip we were to take. *Petrolio* had been translated into Greek, and to celebrate the event Laura would recite poems in Athens and Salonika. At the same time, some photography shows on the cinema of P.P.P. were to open, which had been organized everywhere by the foundation. Finally, there would be some lectures. Laura inserted me into the program, asking me to talk about *Petrolio*, in place of someone who had canceled at the last minute ('Now you're *A CELEBRITY*, am I right? You turn down everybody's sheets!!!'). Massimo Fusillo, a serious scholar, university professor, and friend of Walter Siti, was also supposed to come with us. He was to talk about *Medea,* and he later wrote an important book, titled *Grecia secondo Pasolini* (Greece According to Pasolini*)*. Completing the group was a fellow Laura had dug up somewhere or other, a French semiotician, totally without affect, who spoke in a monotone about the *signes* of Pasolini, *signes du moi* and *signes* of I don't know what, reading entire pages of an interminable essay that, literally, meant nothing outside of his own head.[24] It was in this manner that the singular period of apprenticeship or *school of life* that I had spent, while I rounded the promontory of thirty, in the shadow of the Madwoman reached its final phase in Greece.

The Dionysiac enthusiast sees himself as a satyr, and *as a satyr he in turn sees the god,* i.e. in his transformed state he sees a new vision outside himself which is the Apolline perfection of his state. With this new vision the drama is complete.

FRIEDRICH NIETZSCHE, *The Birth of Tragedy*

The French semiotician was waiting for us in Athens. With Massimo Fusillo I had a perfect understanding from the start of the trip. As a critic and scholar, Massimo is one of those who know their subject. He's an expert in ancient romances, he edited an edition of the *Argonautica* of Apollonius of Rhodes, he's written books on the literary history of certain eternal themes, like that of the double. He is a true connoiseur of opera, cinema, theater. At the time of the journey to Greece I couldn't know it, but Massimo, too, was to all intents and purposes an initiate. Today he's the president of the Leather Club of Rome, a gay association that, besides a passion for leather clothes (as implied by the name), also promotes a variant ('rubber') in which all the garments are strictly of plastic. Massimo's vocation, as I learn from the site of the Leather Club, is that of Master, and one of his preferred practices is spanking. If I'm describing all this it's not for the pleasure of the portrait but because Massimo, too, like the other people I've mentioned up to this point, including the Madwoman, had that familiarity with violence, and especially with sadomasochistic ritual, that allowed him to grasp without misunderstanding what Pasolini had written in *Petrolio*, and the experience of life that had brought him there. For the moment, on Massimo and me fell the difficult undertaking of a trip with the Madwoman. Among her many mental difficulties was an insane fear of flying, which she could overcome only by stuffing herself with food in an extraordinary manner and swallowing a quantity of tranquilizers capable of felling an entire stable. Arriving on the plane, she collapsed into a kind of semi-consciousness, interrupted by brief jolts of restlessness. She told us that it was Félix Guattari, met at the house of some Red Brigade members who had taken refuge in Paris, who taught her to take psychotropic drugs, inviting them into the body like an important guest at a reception. She had had great respect for Guattari, and had become a friend of his when the famous psychiatrist and philosopher, the author, with Gilles Deleuze, of *Anti-Oedipus*, had pushed her into a pool during a summer party in a garden. So it was possible to push the Madwoman into a pool and not only remain alive but become a friend and confidant! In any case, we arrived in Athens with Laura so stunned by benzodiazepine and a complicated digestion that she wasn't even able to smoke or hurl insults at the taxi-driver. We had reserved rooms at the Hotel Grande Bretagne, one of the best in Athens, in Syntagma Square. Between our lectures, the opening of the show, and the preparations for Laura's performance, the days were quite busy, but not so that we couldn't make some tourist rounds. The Madwoman liked Massimo very much, and he led her into a kind of constant flirtatiousness that served to lighten the atmosphere. As for me, as soon as she recovered from the airplane she set out on one of her periods of more open and dangerous hostility. She regretted having brought me, and when I gave her the text of my lecture on *Petrolio* to read, which was to be used for the simultaneous translation, she had given it back to me full of erasures, question marks, pages torn in half. To our great astonishment, one sunny afternoon, already very hot, as it is in Athens in early May, the Madwoman proposed that we climb to the Parthenon with her, right after a high-calorie lunch in a restaurant in the Plaka. We thought she would drop after fifty meters of climbing, but we were wrong. Mysteries of the human body: she proceeded briskly, with a certain agility, stopping to noisily catch her breath. Arriving at the top, however, she didn't want to follow us into the old museum, where the original Caryatids were preserved, and settled herself to observe the expanse of the roofs of Athens, which from the Parthenon spread in every direction, filling one's gaze with an infinity of small houses in pale colors. She sat there smoking, facing the direction of Piraeus, lost in who knows what grim thought. During another pause in setting up the show or in preparing for her performance, we were taken to the meat market, an immense place that made me think of the cave of the Cyclops, lighted by dim bare bulbs. That time, too, after falling silent, she withdrew into herself, into some internal point of her deformed psychic carapace, standing in front of an immense pyramid of cow hearts, which were still dripping blood and seemed to beat with a tenacious and desperate life.

Laura certainly was not without taste, and the green dress she put on the evening of the première in Athens didn't look bad at all. In the afternoon I had been afraid that Massimo's lecture on *Medea* had disturbed her, bringing back the memory of Maria Callas. Enzo Siciliano had told me that in the period of P.P.P.'s infatuation with Maria Callas the Madwoman had suffered from a terrible jealousy, and it was believable. The most atrocious jealousy is that which we feel toward those who have never granted us the right to be jealous, and won't give us the least comfort of feeling a little bit guilty for what they're doing. So *Medea*, the film that came out in 1970, just two years after *Theorem*, for her must have been like a rusty nail stuck in her memory. Even though she had never been on the throne, she had felt dethroned. But Laura, having listened to the lectures without much interest, had concentrated on the performance. Sitting in the empty orchestra of the theater, I had watched her arranging the lights with tremendous care ('They call me Muci Muci, the wizard of the *luci*!'). She had some doubts about whether to insert certain passages of P.P.P. in the program or not. In the end, she left out a piece from *Orgy*. All in all, Laura's performances in Athens and Salonika were not very different from *A Desperate Vitality*, the recital of Pasolini's

146

poetry that she had been performing for several months. Anyone who saw this show will remember it well, even at a distance of many years. It's an art, to bring literary texts to the stage of a theater, and truly very difficult. I'm not talking about the actor who recites a poem—which already requires a minimum of talent, but is manageable. What I'm talking about is an extreme limit reached by few, beyond which the voice, in contact with the written word, creates a new work, literally unprecedented. An incomparable example? Carmelo Bene and Dino Campana. And yet Laura, by completely different means from Carmelo Bene's, reached with Pasolini's poems the same degree of necessity, violence, beauty. The audience of Greek students and Italian residents in Athens were silenced, right from the start, by that sort of suffering evocation. P.P.P.'s lines, passing through the incredible filter of the Madwoman's body, came out with a force of persuasion that I had never felt reading them. As if they were made of a substance of their own, thin but more lasting than the simple vibration of the air, they seemed to hover, suspended in the great space between the audience and the ceiling. They were extracted one by one from a hot, living material like the pyramids of cow hearts we had admired the day before in the meat market. They were the expression of emotions so scorching that they pierced the thick hide of the literary code that cocooned them. They achieved, finally, the greatest of poetry's enchantments: the being there, the real presence—as if it were granted to mortals to return from their own death.

The joys of the sex change, and the deep revelations that derive from it come to the engineer Carlo Valletti, too—the 'first' by education and social privilege. Meanwhile, returning from a new trip to the East, he can't find his double. That serene equilibrium, which lasted for so long, like the most successful family ménage, has dissolved. Sorrow at the loss of one's double is one of the most agonizing sorrows in existence. But Carlo has to resign himself, try to live on his own. We're in May of 1972, in Italy there are elections, and our hero, still young but already well situated on the ladder up the pyramid of power, is increasingly corruptible. During a dinner of powerful men, which is revealed as a kind of mafioso ritual, Carlo 'suddenly stopped feeling his penis as flesh.' At the moment, he hasn't the courage to go and look at himself in the toilet of the Roman restaurant. But the time has come for the *Second fundamental moment of the poem*. As in the case of the other Carlo, a mirror is needed in which to contemplate his own metamorphosis, the new genital organs. And even if P.P.P. doesn't allude to this, it seems legitimate to wonder: mustn't such a vision of the self with the attributes of the other sex be the secret of the mirror of Narcissus? What does Narcissus love? Himself, right. But what does it mean? Mustn't it be that truly looking at oneself, to the extreme limit, means seeing the hidden sex—the ultimate shame and the ultimate resource?

'When Carlo was naked, his eyes fell on the mirror, which showed his reflection; and there, suddenly, the reason for the weight that pressed on his chest and the emptiness that unpleasantly lightened the lower part of his stomach, under the trousers, became clear. In fact, two enormous breasts were sticking out from his chest; and between his legs, in place of the penis, there was an empty space covered by a bush of hair: a vulva.'

(But 'it was in other words,' the narrator adds, 'the words used by the people,' and which the bourgeoisie has never found substitutes for, 'that Carlo became aware of his own sex change.')

The 'virgin Carlo,' as P.P.P. calls him wittily, has a justifiable impatience to experience his new sex. Who knows why greater capacities to enjoy, more intense orgasms are attributed to the new sex, to the *hidden* organ. In *Petrolio*, then, the dangers of pleasure and those of knowledge are intentionally confused. If every metamorphosis is knowledge, the change of sex is perfect knowledge. The desire to complete the process of initiation up to the supreme vision and the sexual itch are not two identical things, but they willingly collaborate toward the same goal. The other Carlo had organized things in a big way, on the field beside Via Casilina. He, instead, concentrates on a single male. That miraculous cosmic energy, first incarnated by twenty erect penises, now is concentrated in a single one, the penis of Carmelo, coat check in the chic restaurant in Rome frequented by Carlo. Carmelo is as hard and proud as a young king who has just been crowned. The setting is the same, with all that that involves: one of the beloved bare fields in the no man's lands on the far periphery of Rome. Roused by the presence of the erect penis, the sense of submission is merged with a joy that has never been expressed with such intensity.

Before leaving for Greece as Laura's escort, I had retrieved the copy of *Petrolio* that Maria had found in Dragan and Ljuda's house. Long stripes of a blue highlighter were the trace of her passage. There had been no quarrel between us, but I foresaw that when I returned from my trip we wouldn't see each other anymore. My timid and faltering attempt to slap her had dissolved into a liberating laugh ('If you do it only to give me pleasure, what's the point?'). Maybe in my darkest and muddiest depths a master was stirring, or a slave, or a two-faced figure, which to the joys of domination could add those of submission. This possibility of changing roles, like everything else, had a precise name: in sadomasochism an anxiety to classify and name operates aggressively. For Maria, as for our Bosnian friends, there was no escape: all humanity, one could claim, was sadomasochistic. Freud had got everything wrong: those games, infinitely more exciting than sex, were the secret fulcrum, made invisible by repression, of becoming personal. To discover one's nature as a master, or as a slave, was equivalent to an awakening that involved the most intimate fibers of being. And it was precisely that which, according to all appearances, had happened to P.P.P. in the last years of his life, when, increasingly alone, he insisted on proceeding in the direction of his desires, relying unhesitatingly on the needle of his tragic compass. Lying on the dusty and decorous quilt of the big bed in my room in the Hotel Grande Bretagne, I read and reread some sentences from Note 65 of *Petrolio*, which the blue ink of Maria's highlighter made appear as if submerged in cold water, in a mountain lake. The most important meaning of the sexual metamorphosis, wrote P.P.P., is that *'being possessed is an experience cosmically opposite to that of possession.'* On the part of the one who is possessed, he who possesses is perceived as a Good, 'even if it involves sacrifice, suffering, humiliation, death.' On the other hand, it's indisputable that the Possessor is 'THE Evil' by antonomasia, therefore being possessed is what is farthest from Evil, or rather is the only possible experience of the Good, as Grace, '*life in its pure, cosmic state.*'

'*The one who is possessed loses consciousness of the shape of the penis, of its limited wholeness, and feels it as an infinite and formless means by which Something or Someone takes possession of him, reduces him to a possession, to a nothing that has no will except to be lost in that different Will which annihilates him.*'

Between the dates of Laura's performance in Athens and those planned for Salonika there was a week's interval. Laura had returned to Italy to shoot some scenes of a film, while Massimo and I would stay in Greece, renting a car and heading north in short stages. The French semiotician had gone back to where he came from. Massimo turned out to be a wonderful companion for that strange forced vacation. The appointment with the Madwoman in Salonika was far enough away to allow us to relax. In those days the Greek spring had reached its point of greatest splendor, and was already besieged by the imminence of burning summer. Stopping wherever we felt like it, we headed toward Verghina, to visit the tombs of the Macedonian kings. Few pictures have had on me an effect so profound and lasting as the fresco of one of these tombs in Verghina, which represents Pluto, driving a chariot, in the act of seizing Persephone, who, arms raised to the sky, on her back and half naked, invokes aid in vain. Evidently, we can look at and even appreciate an enormous number of works of art, but only a very few of these, for reasons fated to remain obscure, have the power to strike us, to besiege us by force in our sensibility and our defense systems.

I still didn't know anything about the hidden but

tenacious ties between *Petrolio* and the story of Persephone, torn from her mother Demeter and forced to rule in the Underworld as the wife of Pluto, the god of the dead, the lord of the lower depths. But certainly that fresco, hidden for centuries in a tomb, was, no less than Pasolini's last work, the product of a vision, of a radical illumination, and, at a distance of many centuries, it transmitted, still intact, the emotion of knowledge and the vertigo of the arcane. The painter of Verghina was an artist sensitive to the contrast between force and beauty, violence and defenselessness. Pluto is a hunter intoxicated by the joy of the prey, a rapist at the peak of excitement. Curly yellow hair and beard surround his face, dulled by lust, like the locks of a wild beast. With one hand he holds the reins of the two mighty horses yoked to the chariot, with the other he squeezes one of Proserpina's breasts. In trying to resist the abduction, the girl has lost her dress, only a last shred clings to her hips, and who knows for how much longer. The expression on her face is desolate and at the same time frightened. A moment earlier, she was carelessly picking flowers, with her friends, in a place that some call 'the plains of Nysa' and which for other ancient writers is Sicily. And now she has become the prey, naked in a chariot, at the mercy of the hunter. According to the oldest and most authoritative version of the myth, in the *Hymn to Demeter*, Persephone was picking flowers with the daughters of Ocean, 'buxom girls,' and the painter of Verghina had painted one of these companions kneeling on the ground, she, too, with her arms raised in a vain cry for help, terrorized by the appearance of the god and the kidnapping of her friend, and almost suffocated by the dust raised by the big wheels of the chariot.

After Verghina, Massimo and I headed for Chalkidiki, that peninsula vaguely similar to a comb made of bone corroded by salt, or a letter of the alphabet of an extinct language. At the expense of the Pasolini Foundation, we stayed in a nice hotel with a pool, already open for the summer season, waiting until we had to go to Salonika. The prospect of returning to the clutches of the Madwoman certainly didn't excite us. Massimo, to tell the truth, enjoyed privileged treatment, but he suffered like the others during the blow-ups. Furthermore, when it came time to move to Salonika, we found her in the worst mood, depressed and aggressive. In the city there was an atmosphere of patriotic agitation. The adversary, for once, wasn't the eternal Turkey but Macedonia, which, just born out of the collapse of the former Yugoslavia, had reclaimed its ancient borders, including a good slice of northern Greece. Balkan nonsense, which also involved some famous archeological find. A few days before our arrival, an immense demonstration had paraded through Salonika, carrying banners that, in place of the usual slogans, bore quotations from Herodotus and Thucydides. One evening at dinner a literature professor from the university tried to convince Laura of the absurdity and injustice of the Macedonian claims, gradually growing heated as the Greeks do when they talk about things dear to them. When we least expected it, Laura had overwhelmed him with an avalanche of insults, brandishing a fish fork—the tiny trident of an immense, deformed Neptune. *She knew it well*, all this Fascist nonsense about countries, about nations. 'All the little men need a mamma who works to support them and when necessary *spanks them*. And without *fear of the mamma*, they really can't live. Am I right, little slut? Behind every criminal, kidnapper of children, well-known louse ... *there's his mamma who approves*, who is happy with her child. You keep them, these mammas, these countries.' That very evening, as we left the restaurant, the conversation now reduced to a prudent muteness, and returned to the hotel, walking along the narrow streets around the port, we ran into an acrobat, a street artist who was performing his act in the corner of a small open space. In itself, this act wasn't very astonishing: the acrobat climbed up an unsteady tower of stools that he himself constructed as he advanced upward. But the man must have been at least sixty: he was thin and muscular, with an aquiline nose, his face marked by a spider web of delicate wrinkles. The real show consisted in the fact that a man could still perform the act at that age. The muscles of his slender, tense body were straining so hard that they trembled slightly, and everything he did he did at the outer limit of his capacities, slowly, compensating with concentration, one would have said, for the strength that failed him. This personal challenge to time and the force of gravity was destined, obviously, to defeat. It was possible that what we were seeing was the last act to be performed by that bony and exhausted acrobat, in his black t-shirt, the pants clinging to his still agile legs. And yet there he was: sovereign of the moment, in perfect equilibrium. Laura was entranced by the unexpected performance, wedging herself into the front row of the semicircle formed by the spectators, all chance passersby like us. When at last the man ended his show, she began to dig in her purse, and then, approaching the overturned collection hat, stuck a fat roll of drachmas in it—much more than the acrobat had ever earned in a single performance, as a young man or an old one. That distant grandson of Kafka's 'Hunger Artist' had truly subjugated her, so much that, until we got to the hotel, the Madwoman was turned inward, putting a heavy lid on her boiling caldron. To the nobility or the suffering of others she could be very sensitive or completely indifferent, without any predictable method or criterion. She, so different in body and character, was, suddenly, *reflected* in the old acrobat, as if before her eyes she found not a poor flesh and blood type who was trying to earn some money but a prophecy, a living allegory, a revelatory hallucination. The next afternoon, while Laura was reading Pasolini's lines in the great hall of the University of Salonika, that scene returned to mind, and she, too, seemed to me at the limit of her strength, engaged for the last time in lifting herself above herself, pivoting on her own voice as if on some piece of athletic equipment, seeking a final redemption from gravity and the tedium of days that had passed forever.

For the man to become a woman: that is the supreme, the perfect, the crucial metamorphosis. It's the narrow door that any truly effective process of initiation has to pass through. In *Petrolio*, the order of events can at times seem tangled, but from the point of view of the initiation and the possession of reality they fit perfectly, each is the consequence of the next. Everything becomes clearer the moment we accept that we're reading this final work of Pasolini, in all senses a will, *as a rite rather than as a novel*. If the sexual metamorphosis completes the initiation, that, in turn, has to lead to its supreme goal, which is not an abstract concept but a *vision*. In the vision it happens like a purifying fire, or the extraction of an essence, and reality appears free of dross, for what it is. And it's precisely for that reason that the initiate can say of himself that he was born a second time, because in fact it's a new world, incomparably truer than the one he has always lived in, the one he has now reached, never to turn back. In *Petrolio*, which is a work based entirely on the idea of the double and of duplicity, the supreme vision, too, is double. Carlo the Second, who has always lived his humble and lustful life amid the people, is fated to have a complete knowledge of the 'ugliness' and of the 'repulsiveness' of humanity in the period of false tolerance and consumerism. The vision takes place in a precise place in Rome, 'the crossroads of Via Casilina with Via Torpignattara and Via Torpignattara itself with the first twenty cross streets, to the right and the left, starting from the intersection and moving in the direction of Via Tuscolana.' It's the popular heart of a Rome that, starting after the war, first with the suburbs and then with the new neighborhoods built on speculation, extended southward, in the enormous slice of the city included between the two ancient roads, the Casilina and the Tuscolana. A fairly grandiose scene to function as a credible image of the entire world, of the terrifying everywhere. To name what happened in this scene P.P.P., in the last years of his life, had often used the gravest, most catastrophic, most irreparable of words: genocide. Yes, gen-o-cide. The jobs that the Nazis assigned to the concentration camps were now done by supermarkets. Starting at a certain point, advertising had replaced the vast rallies and the secret police. Fashion was now enthroned securely at the head of the crowds of Death. In the last years of his life, Pasolini never stopped beating on that drum. This he has in his mind, this he feels night after night, when he wanders around the outskirts of the city, seeking the ecstasy of submission, which of all types of ecstasy is surely the most dangerous. His point of view is not that of the intellectual who ages amid books and papers, suffocated by words, but that of the soul in pain, the roving character who every night goes to bed very late, who needs to extinguish his desire. And it's thus that he becomes aware of it. As if a city, by the sole fact of being frequented at unusual hours, were disposed to reveal secret information, tearing the veil of illusions that rock us in our sleep. Like a character in a catastrophic science-fiction book, a Philip Dick[25] nightmare, P.P.P. discovered the horrendous truth that lies hidden behind appearances, and knocks at the doors of his neighbors to communicate his discoveries before someone arrives to kill him. We have to insist on the mode of acquaintance, which is physical before intellectual, and is the direct consequence of a style of life, not of a system of thoughts and definitions. The intellectual, the writer, in general is an individual who possesses a body like everyone else, and can enjoy it like everyone else, but at the moment of knowledge knows only with his mind, while P.P.P. throws every centimeter into the fray, every gram of his flesh, lets himself be saturated by the flow of life like a sponge. But what is it, exactly, that he discovered and has such a need to reveal? What has he done so that bodies, individuals, lives have lost every grace, every beauty, as if they were victims of a powerful enchantment? The old humanity was being rapidly replaced by a demented and monstrous species never seen before. Like a population of aliens who, under a human appearance, harbor only dark purposes of destruction and dominion. He, P.P.P., can't stop sounding the alarm. Even if it was the last thing he did in life. In particular, the *Lutheran Letters* and *Corsair Writings* can be considered real accounts of the genocide. *Salò*, too, is permeated with this terminal vision: in it fascism is demonstrated even too transparently as the root, the foundation on which consumer society is erected. In *Petrolio*, finally, the vision becomes grandiose, like a blockbuster with hundreds of extras, complex scenic machinery, stratagems of lights and colors. What is revealed to the eyes of Carlo, to his vision—which the initiation has made acute, as if an angel's wing had brushed the delicate and resistant eyelids, lifting them off his eyes—is an apocalyptic end of the line of humanity, the complete and conclusive stage of its degradation. In the Gironi and Bolge of this anthropological inferno, the various aspects of the 'ugliness' and the 'repulsiveness' of this new humanity pass before Carlo's eyes, just as they appear in the bodies, or in the way of dressing, in the neurosis, in respectability and the feeling of 'dignity', in cowardice, in false tolerance, in the imitation of the tenor of bourgeois life, and in all the other repulsive variants of universal conformity. Pasolini, writing on these subjects, had never found an eloquence so high, such a desperate force of persuasion. And an atmosphere of special sacredness isn't alien to the result. The whole story is strewn with precise allusions to an ancient mystery rite, the most celebrated and yet the most secret in all antiquity, which is celebrated at Eleusis, at the gates of Athens, every year between September and October. The ceremonies are so ancient that their origins are lost in the most obscure ambiguities of myth, and no one can say how and when they reached the land of Athens, coming perhaps from Crete. With a series of very precise allusions *Petrolio* aimed at renewing the memory of this ancient Greek cult, founded on initiation, on the metamorphosis of the individual which produces the supreme knowledge, contained in the vision. It wasn't a simple learned citation, a pointless archeological embellishment. If anything, P.P.P. had discovered, in these ancient experiences, a reflection of his own, and vice versa. As if he were, strictly speaking, *the last of the ancients*, he had leaned out over the abyss, had grasped the supreme reality and, so to speak, the reality of reality. Like *Petrolio*, finally, the ancient mystery rite involved a broad use of symbols of the male sex and the female, in a perpetual game of equivalences and confusions. There is game and game: the one that confuses the two sexes, camouflages each with the semblances of the other, and unites them in a superior identity is a very powerful game, one might say an effective magic. Like looking in a magic mirror, at the motionless surface of a miraculous fountain. It is P.P.P. himself who warns readers: it's a 'long tradition of mysteries' that provides him with the model for the initiation adventure of his hero, Carlo Valletti, and his double. When this tradition erupts in *Petrolio*, the impression is that the writer has collected an archeological find and has inserted it there, in *something written*, without even worrying about dusting it off, making it comprehensible. Returning home, at the end of the vision that has completed his journey of initiation, Carlo the Second notices a tabernacle, which contains an extraordinary image: 'a monstrous woman, consisting of two stocky legs, between which, in place of the groin, a huge woman's head was embedded—so that the crack of the vulva coincided with the break in the chin.' The monster holds, in her right hand, 'a long stick, as tall as she is': without any possible doubt, it's 'a long, knotty penis.' It would be very hard to understand what P.P.P. is talking about if we hadn't at hand the illustration that he, too, was looking at. It's the image that appears on the cover of a book by Alfonso di Nola, entitled *Antropologia religiosa* (Religious Anthropology), published by Vallecchi in 1974.[26] The strange drawing represents a gastrocephalic statuette, as they are called by archeologists, discovered in the sanctuary of Demeter and Kora in Priene, and going back at least to the fourth century before Christ. These terracotta idols, Di

Nola explains in words clearer than Pasolini's, represent 'the lower part of a female human figure deformed in such a way that the pelvis, the belly, the vulva, and the thighs come, in their totality, to represent a female head which the legs stand right under, with the absence of the middle area of the thorax and the stomach' ('the hair that crowns the figure,' furthermore, is simply 'the modification and adaptation of the raised dress'). Without resorting to the mystery tradition, it would be very difficult to understand not only the appearance of the 'woman monster' of Note 74 but Pasolini's allusions in the following note (74A). Starting with the inscription ('I've erected this statue in order to laugh') carved into the pedestal of the tabernacle. The 'archeological citation,' as P.P.P. himself calls it, finds its explanation in a mystery tradition in which, in legends and the most ancient rituals, laughter is connected to the display of symbols of male and female genital organs. *Aporreta simbola*, Pasolini clarifies, meticulously, that is, 'unspeakable,' subject to the ban of silence, since the knowledge revealed in these rites is reserved to the initiates alone. P.P.P. used not only the cover of Di Nola's *Antropologia religiosa*. In the first chapter of the book, titled *Riso e oscenità* (Laughter and Obscenity), a myth whose versions can be traced back not only in Greece but in ancient Egypt and even Japan was reconstructed. Wherever it's found, the story is repeated identically in its basic elements: a dangerous cosmic crisis is thwarted by the intervention of a woman (a goddess or a mortal) who at the right moment lifts up her clothes, displaying her vagina, and provoking in this way a hilarity that saves the world, discharging the accumulated tension. When Pasolini reads those pages, his work on *Petrolio* is already very far along, but that old story seems to him a confirmation, a ray of light from the past that illuminates what he himself is doing.

The last morning we spent together in Salonika, the Madwoman wanted to visit with Massimo and me the ancient convents perched on the hills surrounding the city and the port. By chance I had read in a story in Russian literature that it was precisely in those convents near Salonika that the Cyrillic alphabet was established, and I didn't mind that pilgrimage within the walls and cloisters where the language of *War and Peace*, of *The Idiot*, of *Doctor Zhivago* originated. As she had some days earlier, during the visit to the Parthenon, Laura amazed us with her agility. The presence of Massimo, I had observed, stirred her up, had the power to rouse in her an almost flirtatious manner. I, too, in a sense enjoyed it, because in front of him she didn't give in to the usual scenes and sadistic repertory. Then we had only to be alone for a few minutes to make up for lost time. But I knew that these were the last days of work at the Pasolini Foundation. At every opportunity the Madwoman hissed that, as soon as we returned from Greece we would finally have a meeting about the interviews, 'and the whole truth will out!' So I enjoyed that last show. With that courtesy toward women of a certain age that only Neapolitans can take to the ultimate degree of perfection, Massimo offered his arm to Laura, and the tour of the convents was really lovely, marked by cigarette breaks during which we took in the view of the gulf and, in the middle of the port, the famous tower, the symbol of the city. At a certain point, in a completely surprising way, she asked us to leave her alone in a church we had visited, but not to go too far away. We sat down to wait for her outside in the small stone church square, leaning against a white marble well of the Byzantine era. The door of the church was open, so, against the background of icons with the magnetic faces of prophets and apostles, we could glimpse the profile of Laura, concentrated, as far as one could say, if not in a prescribed prayer in some delicate spiritual meditation. It's possible that two large tears, behind the screen of her dark glasses, had begun to furrow her sagging cheeks. All this, Massimo and I commented, seemed a contradiction in terms. How could someone like the Madwoman pray, in what language, and to ask for what? After remaining absorbed like that for a while, and faintly sighing, she put an offering in a box, as generous as the one she'd left in the old acrobat's hat, and in exchange took from a pile a single candle, one of those long, very slender ones that are used in the Greek churches. She brought it to the flame of another that was already lit and planted it in the bowl of sand, then the desire for a cigarette prevailed over mysticism, and she tore herself away from those low warm lights, from the decorations of gold and silver, from the narcotic flow of incense, to join us outside. 'The break is over,' she said, joining us at the center of the square. It was a phrase she repeated often, almost automatically, returning to others after a brief absence. Among the many cards in her pack, this woman also possessed the ironic knowledge that she was unbearable.

The last engagement we had in Salonika was the presenta-
tion of the new Greek translation of *Petrolio*. With that taken
care of, we got in the car to head to Athens, I at the wheel, the
Madwoman next to me, and the adored Massimo, who was
almost starting to rouse some jealousy in me, in the back
seat. But, thanks to his presence, the trip, in itself long and
tiring because of the bad roads, was pleasant enough. Massimo had understood that one of the best ways to tame the
Madwoman was to bombard her with questions, transforming the conversation into a kind of permanent interview.
Once induced to rummage in the big bag of memories, she
didn't stop, amazing herself with the treasures she found.
Everything essential, in her past, seemed to have happened
at night, in an intoxicating and exciting atmosphere of
promiscuity, experiment, provocation. For years and years,
there had never been anything boring, no cloud of disap-
pointment and disenchantment appeared on the horizon.
P.P.P. was the principal star of this happy world, which had
the ability, like certain enchantments in fables, to pretend
that it was eternal. And yet it wasn't at all. The awakening had
been very harsh: like after the worst of drunks, and destined
to remain such, without any respite. The death of P.P.P. had
to do with it and didn't. The truth, Laura told us while the

Greek spring, along the roadside, did everything possible to show us its beauties and its dreams of forgetfulness, '*the truth is that getting old is always terrible*, and if someone tells you the contrary he's lying, but I can't lie, I'm not ashamed to admit it, they may have a more or less decorous appearance, but *inside people of my age are all like me, the happy old folks are only on TV.*' While I was driving, that stupefying vision of humanity took possession of my admiring mind: well, yes, one had only to get old to feel growing inside one's own personal Madwoman. One could exercise, eat less, stop smoking, find someone to spend the rest of one's life with. Or not: simply be like Laura. Make the external correspond to the internal. And now it's your turn, she added: you have your ten, your fifteen years ahead. 'You're young, you're clever, you can make it. But to *really* make it you need rage. Pier Paolo at a certain point understood that, rage is more important than talent, talent any little bourgeois can have it, rage no, rage is a rare gift, you have to cultivate it, it's like having a big dick or a sharp mind, or both—which is always better, am I right?'

When we reached Athens, it was already late afternoon. Unexpectedly, the lobby of the Grande Bretagne had been transformed into a piece of contemporary Italy, euphoric and childish. It was May 18th, and that very evening, in the stadium in Athens, the final of the Champions League was to be played between Milan and Barcelona.[27] Under the big crystal chandeliers a small crowd of Milan fans congregated, with the look of Fininvest or Mediaset executives, excited about the match, simple, unsophisticated types, soaked with cologne or aftershave, the knots of their regimental ties as big as a fist, and excessively loud (at that time people still thought that to speak on a mobile phone you had to shout). In their company were some of the most beautiful women I've ever seen, in dresses as light as veils of dew over perfect figures, tiny sequined purses dangling from slender wrists, and feet in heels thinner than the stem of a champagne glass. There it is, right in front of us, as if on a carnival float, the new race of the *inheritors of the world*. All the power of the masters married to the subtle, impalpable charisma of the servants; all the docility of housewives joined to the irony, the savoir faire, the sense of opportunity of truly deluxe whores. The Italian race reached, in that group of wealthy fans, at an away game with their companions, an

incomparable point of evolution and—I feel like adding—
of tragic beauty. Centuries of buffoonery, of cold-blooded
murder, of dissembling and unscrupulousness had led to
that result which, from the secure stronghold of the present,
didn't hide its aims of conquest of the future. In compact
formation, Massimo and I, on either side as guardians of
Laura's body, cut through the small crowd to the reception desk. Until that moment, thanks to Massimo, she had
been a perfect traveling companion, but the sight of those
people had in a few seconds unnerved her. 'What the fuck
do they want,' she hissed as she proceeded, 'what the fuck
are these louts shouting about.' If we had been in a comic
strip, thunderbolts and skulls would have been crowding
over her head, meaning a bad mood ready to explode. And,
punctually, it exploded, when the desk clerk tried to prove
to her that there were *two*, not *three*, rooms reserved. In her
best French, she began to inveigh at a volume so loud that
it silenced the big ties and their whores. The manager of the
Grande Bretagne arrived in person, and in some way the
situation was resolved. Again we made our way through the
perfumed, well-dressed crowd of Milan fans. 'Brava, Signora
Betti!' a fellow older than the others said to her, just to say
something. 'Fuck off,' she answered, heading straight for the
elevator. Massimo had stayed at the reception desk to take
care of some business. And as soon as the door of the elevator closed the Madwoman began to behave strangely, lifting
her enormous skirt and rummaging with her other arm in
that mountain of fabric and flesh as if she were adjusting
something. Then, slightly bent over, she made a sign to me
to be quiet, her gaze indecipherable behind the dark lenses.
There are moments when you really wonder if you're awake

or dreaming, and such is the marvel of what you see that the reality in fact appears made of the material of dreams. Yes, the Madwoman was taking revenge on who knows what personal outrage had been done to her in the lobby. Can you imagine the sound of pee falling on the carpet in an elevator of a grand hotel? When we left the elevator the stain was there, it was just what it seemed: a signature, an outrage, the whim of an old child-whale who doesn't want to accept the existence of those she detests—or who perhaps instill fear.

One thing should not be forgotten: Pasolini wasn't at all interested in citing the initiation rites of the Eleusinian Mysteries to create a kind of learned, purely evocative atmosphere. While he's writing *Petrolio*, or shooting *Salò*, he's gone farther, not as one who is exploring but as one who will never return home. *Petrolio* is the *live-broadcast* chronicle of an initiation, or rather: of a taking possession of reality. First the doubling, and then the sexual metamorphosis, as we've already said many times, are the conditions under which a new vision becomes possible. As far as Carlo the Second is concerned, the scene of this vision is in the heart of working class Rome, decimated by the consumer genocide. The other Carlo, too, the powerful engineer Valletti, in order to approach the supreme knowledge, has, at the peak of his career, had to become a woman, taste the joys of submission. And here he is ready: but in a very different environment from the intersection of Via Casilina and Via Torpignattara. We are at the Quirinal, no less, packed with powerful people for the Festival of the Republic.[28] We can define quite clearly and concisely what the initiation will allow us to grasp: the game of hidden forces that rule the world. It's not coincidental, then, if the crucial episode of this journey takes place at the Quirinal, on the occasion of a reception at which practically all the powerful of Italy are gathered, and reviewed by Carlo from first to last, from the Communist Berlinguer to the neo-Fascist Pino Rauti. It's only at the end of this portrait gallery that Carlo enters a more intimate and quiet space, a kind of small living room—'a peaceful corner, outside the hellish throng' of the reception. The people gathered in this place are intent on listening to someone who is telling a story. They have nothing in common with the others invited to the reception. It's still a matter, on the other hand, of 'bourgeois Italians'—to be exact, 'literary men, with their wives.' Curious, Carlo takes a place among them, while the narrator ends his story, handing it off to someone else. Before starting in his turn to speak, this new narrator presents a basic premise—'*The narrative art, as you well know, is dead. We are in mourning. Therefore, dear listeners, in the absence of wine you must content yourselves with kykeon.*' As in the case of the 'woman monster,' the gastrocephalic statue that ends the vision of Shit, the allusion to the rite of the Eleusinian Mysteries is so precise as to be incomprehensible to the majority of readers. Kykeon is the drink that initiates to the Mysteries drank, at the end of the ritual fasting and the long procession from Athens to Eleusis, before entering the sanctuary. Probably it was a psychotropic substance, a hallucinogen that encouraged the supreme vision. Not coincidentally, it was Albert Hofmann, the inventor of LSD, who investigated its chemical composition. But kykeon isn't just one among many elements of the Eleusinian rites. It appears in the myth that is the precondition, the eternal model to imitate. Just as it is handed down to us in the *Hymn to Demeter*, the goddess, not resigned to the loss of her daughter Persephone, who has been kidnapped by Pluto, abandons Olympus and wanders the world of men, exhausted by grief, in search of a reunion with her. It's in this situation that Demeter arrives at Eleusis, and is welcomed, without being recognized, in the house of the noble Celeus and his wife, Deianira. When the latter offers her some wine, without hesitation Demeter refuses it. Mourning for the loss of Persephone compels her to stay away from it. In place of the wine, she has kykeon prepared, revealing to her mortal host the recipe—water, barley flour, 'delicate mint.' The art of narrative is dead, says the character in *Petrolio* before starting to tell his story. We, too, are in mourning, like Demeter who has lost her daughter Persephone, and in place of wine we must be content with kykeon. But in this privation an unprecedented possibility is hidden. Kykeon makes possible the *unmediated* vision of the truth. All those who were initiated into the Eleusinian Mysteries had to drink it before being admitted to the highest degree of mysteric knowledge, in the heart of the sanctuary. Merged with the darkness, the frightening sounds, the solemnity of the rites, the exertion of walking from Athens and fasting, the hallucinogenic effect of the kykeon was such as to leave a profound and lasting impression in the mind.

The flight that would take us to Rome left from the Athens Airport right after lunch. For the Madwoman, that meant starting to fill up with food and barbiturates around eleven. Next to the lobby of the Grande Bretagne was a Chinese restaurant that was open all day. Laura ordered practically the whole menu, forcing Massimo and me, who had just had a normal breakfast, to have at least something to keep her company. She inhaled large amounts of spring rolls, soy noodles, chicken with almonds, beef with black mushrooms, and then prepared to confront her aeronautic nirvana. For a few long minutes during the flight, seeing her supine, motionless and openmouthed, on the capacious seat in first class, I believed she was dead. A thought far from baseless: but her time had not yet come. Mine, on the other hand, as consultant and contributor at the Pasolini Foundation, had. I remember well that return to Rome because I had the impression that everything in my life, in that short absence, had changed irrevocably. Dragan and Ljuda had abandoned the house in Trastevere, to move to Milan, where they had other friends able to help them. In the summer of 1995, as soon as the siege of Sarajevo was over, they returned home, continuing to plan their performance based on *Salò*. Maria had followed them, and had written me a letter of farewell. I've always felt a great affection for all the people in my life who remained at the stage of possibility, of roads not taken, transforming themselves rapidly into vague memories, or faint hallucinations. I wouldn't know how to say why, but in everything that I could have lived, and didn't, I recognize a credible image, the only one I can conceive, of Eternity. I hope Maria found many strong, determined men, who were able to beat her the way and as much as she wanted.

My first book, meanwhile, had begun to circulate, with some success and an unexpected number of good reviews. I had for so long absorbed the Madwoman's sarcasm, her contempt for me and my aspirations, that every so often, in spite of such a positive situation, I had the suspicion of a false step, or a false departure. But what is done is done, and I would never become P.P.P., if I lived a million years. Just before leaving, I had brought to the foundation a copy of the book for Laura, with an affectionate dedication. A few hours later, in the course of a tirade whose cause I no longer remember, she had ripped it, thrown it on the floor, and trampled it, like a cigarette butt, and ultimately that seemed to me a good baptism, to balance with the long, favorable review in the *Corriere della Sera*. I can still remember the torn cover on the floor of the reading room of the foundation, furtively contemplated by a terrified visitor, ignorant of the meaning of that ritual quartering. Then, as I recounted at the start of this memoir, the day of settling accounts arrived, of the assault with the box cutter, the farewell. Leaving my key in plain sight, I went down the stairs of the big building at the corner of Piazza Cavour for the last time, with that indefinable feeling (balanced between euphoria and regret) that we feel when we realize that an epoch of life has just passed forever.

In spite of the death of the art of narration the fact remains that those who drink kykeon, in the initiation story of Carlo at the Quirinal, are *narrators*. To judge from what remains to us of *Petrolio* Carlo hears eight stories, which we could call initiation stories—of one, the fourth, only the title remains. It's worth recalling the contents of this little Decameron:

The story of a man and his body
The story of the reconstruction of a story
The story of a thousand and one characters
The story of four critics and four painters
The story of a father and his two daughters
The story of two fathers and two sons
The story of a cosmic flight
The story of the slaughters

The first narrator is a 'witty man,' used to being liked by his fellows. In tails, he looks like 'a big ant dressed as a man,' or 'the voice of conscience.' His story is 'a parable,' and the meaning of this parable is 'the relationship of an author to the form he creates'—or, rather, 'the absolute independence of laws that establish a form with respect to the laws of all other forms.'

'Though it is hallucinatory,' the second narrator states, on the other hand, you mustn't believe that *The story of a thousand and one characters* 'is any less real.' But the third narrator's level of consciousness is even more advanced. He asks his listeners, before starting on *The story of two fathers and two sons*, to allow him some words of introduction, to play down 'the tragic moment of the beginning.' The fact is that 'storytelling endangers existence and thus throws it into confusion. The narrating subject, faced with his own opening sentence, enters a state of crisis.' And it's a real crisis, typical of relations with the sacred. 'The story is within the sacred enclosure.' This danger imposes a ritual, inspired by the requirement to laugh about it. As with savages, there's a need for 'clownish little acts, silly gestures.'

'The rectum teaches the bladder conservation, and the bladder in turn teaches the rectum generosity.' As others might put their work in the shadow of an aesthetic theory or a political or moral philosophy, the third narrator literally cites *Thalassa*, a book by Sándor Ferenczi published in 1924. In it, the brilliant Hungarian follower of Freud attempted a surprising 'psychoanalysis of the origins of sexual life,' which from the story of the individual jumps, in a dizzying series of broadening horizons, to that of the entire species, so that biology and psychology illuminate one another. But what is the meaning of this mutual and virtuous collaboration, through which the rectum teaches the bladder something of its ability to conserve, while the bladder suggests to the rectum a greater willingness to evacuate? Everything makes us think, Ferenczi explains in the first chapter of his work, that only the 'effective cooperation' of the innervations of the anus and the urethra allows a normal ejaculation. In premature ejaculation, instead, only the urethral component, with its tendency to evacuate, is manifested, and in delayed ejaculation the anal component, oriented to retention, prevails. Even if the urethral tendency to evacuation 'always leads to final victory,' ejaculation with the tendency to retention is a permanent struggle. But in the evolution of the individual, as Freud had already explained in *Three Essays on Sexuality*, he establishes the genital area as pre-eminent, to the detriment of other forms of enjoyment. See how the child, to gain the love of his parents, gradually gives up the pleasure of evacuating urine and holding on to feces. These two forms of the erotic do not disappear completely but fuse into a 'superior unity'—the process is called by Ferenczi an *anfimixi*. We have to repeat again: the taste for quotation, which will become rampant, the encyclopedia of knowledge in novelistic sauce are utterly alien to P.P.P., in *Petrolio*. That unbearable fake-erudite pap which characterizes postmodern culture would have simply disgusted him. He doesn't quote but embodies, tests, experiments. And Ferenczi's theory of ejaculation corresponds to what is, probably, the most profound and conclusive of his final intuitions: *the work and the ejaculation are the same thing.* In the end, *something written* will have to be like a warm stain of sperm sprayed on the face of the world.

While the fourth narrator prepares to pour himself his glass of kykeon, he observes that, up to that point, in all the stories that have been told '*the same story is repeated*,' more or less disguised. They are fictions, symbolic forms that clothe a single real, historical, well-defined fact. The title of this 'primal story,' which is never told as such but shines through and is glimpsed by all the others, could be *The story of a failed coup d'état*. Well, the narrator continues, the time has come to take a step further. Let's suppose that for Carlo, who is present at the gathering of narrators, it will be the supreme vision—an experience similar to that of the initiates of Eleusis at the moment when, having performed all the other ritual duties, they are admitted by the priests into the most secluded and secret part of the sanctuary. The story that is about to begin, entitled *The story of the slaughters*, does not refer, obliquely and symbolically, to that untold 'primal story'—on the contrary, *it is it*. Literally. So that the indirect and allusive commentary on that story will have meaning, the direct commentary must, in the end—with the proper precautions taken—assert itself, as evidence. If there were not that pivot, the entire linguistic universe that *something written* consists of would shatter, like a body without a skeleton, an allegory without its literal meaning. The story has as its protagonist the narrator himself, a man without financial worries, whose hobby is folk music. Armed with a sophisticated tape recorder, he finds himself in Katmandu on the evening of an important celebration. Infected by the enthusiasm of the crowd, he lets himself be guided to a small temple in the fields, outside the city, goal of a sort of pilgrimage. Near this small rural temple he is suddenly struck by an unexpected sound: a lament that comes from a bush, near which he has settled with the intention of recording the chants and music of the procession. And in fact there is a man in the thicket of bamboo stalks, so gravely wounded that he is now near the end of his life. He's a Westerner, an American. He was attacked by a group of men because, some hours earlier, he had treated a child harshly. But the story isn't completely believable. In any case, realizing that the narrator is Italian, he wishes to make a confession, before dying. He, too, is of Italian origin, and belongs, in some undefined way, to the Mafia. What he has to recount is 'a brief period of recent Italian history'—no more than six years. The tape recorder is running. 'Everything he told me is recorded on a tape,' the narrator notes, 'mixed with the obsessive ringing of those bells and the Nepalese music, which continued to echo in that cold, dark stretch of countryside under the looming mountains.'

We would expect, at this point, that our narrator would reveal at least something of the story of the dying Italian-American (a mafioso? a C.I.A. agent? both?), which he has recorded. And instead, reaching the edge of revelation, the story is interrupted[29]—it's P.P.P. himself who closes the quotation marks. And, besides, if the interruption was unintentional, like so many others in *Petrolio*, at least part of the confession of an interesting character on the point of death would be preserved. In place of this story, only a few lines of notes remain, written by hand, which *deliberately* make things even more ambiguous and complicated. From these notes we learn, however, that the story begins with 'Kennedy's murder' and that, beyond America, Greece is also involved. The Italian-American, in turn, has heard what he is reporting from someone who also was on the point of death. And so on, in a kind of chain of dying men. In the act of narrating he insists over and over on the fact that there are '*two* phases of the slaughters, *two*.' And, in the tranquility of the little salon in the Quirinal, the narrator repeats to his listeners with the same emphases: '*Two* phases, there are *two*.' There is little else: arriving at the ultimate stage of the secret, *something written* leaves its readers with nothing. But reserved for them, let's remember, is only the chronicle of an initiation—not the initiation itself. In other words: Carlo, unlike us, has heard the entire story.

I imagine that Laura forgot about me with animal-like speed. It always ended like that with people who, for one reason or another, were no longer within range. She knew hatred at a distance, certainly, but if someone escaped her she looked around in search of a new victim. As for me, I literally crossed the street if I met her, pretending not to see her. Once, walking with a friend in the neighborhood of Piazza della Moretta, not far from her apartment, I saw her quarreling with a shopkeeper, who was complaining because Laura had parked her car in front of his display window. '*Don't play the populist,*' she said to him, instead of apologizing. I think she remained like that, fierce and indomitable, until the end—I hope so for her sake. She would never have imagined, I think, the feelings of gratitude I had for her, and the many occasions I would have, over the years, to reflect on that speech about rage she had made in the car, that afternoon in 1994, as I was driving toward Athens on the terrible Greek highway, careful not to be swept away by some truck driver drunk on ouzo. Well, yes—I thought many times—the Madwoman was right, rage is the most important thing, not ideas, not talent first of all but rage. There's a bond so profound between rage and creation that all other bonds pale in comparison, seem superficial, less necessary. So that, in the end, the more you think and the more you begin to glimpse a truth that goes beyond art, a more absolute truth, you begin to conceive rage as the true substance of the world, its possibility of existing, its quintessence.

The myth of Demeter and the lexicon of the ritual of the Mysteries return in the *Fourth fundamental moment of the poem*, corresponding to Note 127 of *Petrolio*. As has already happened for his double, for Carlo the First, too, the moment comes to return to the male sex. The episode happens in Turin, and is connected to the disastrous events that take place in that city, where a bomb destroyed the station. A frightening pain in his stomach forces Carlo to take refuge in the toilet of a bar. While he's shut up inside, in spite of the pain, he is possessed by 'an uncontainable joy.' In front of the mirror in the toilet, Carlo rapidly undresses, as is natural. Much less obvious is the definition that Pasolini gives the gesture, writing that Carlo completes 'the rite of *anasyrma*.' It's the exposing of the female genitals to a divinity, for the purpose of provoking benevolence and laughter, and, in certain legends, of warding off tremendous cosmic crises. A typical *anasyrma* is the one recounted by Herodotus regarding the celebration in honor of the Egyptian cat goddess Bastet, in Subasti, in the Nile delta. And an *anasyrma* is what, according to a particular variant of the Demeter myth, puts the goddess in a good mood by inducing her to drink kykeon, the drink of the Mysteries. But in the *anasyrma* recounted in *Petrolio* there is, in place of the grieving and angry divinity, only the mirror of a public toilet, in which the end of a revelatory metamorphosis appears, and of an entire process of initiation. It is 'with profound emotion' that Carlo 'saw that his chest was a flat chest, without breasts; and, pulling down his pants and underpants ... saw that dangling down below his belly again, under the thin hair, was his old penis.' From the *Third fundamental moment of the poem* we learned that Carlo the Second, returning to the male sex, as will happen to his double, had decided to castrate himself. The second part of *Petrolio* is too fragmentary to understand in detail the fate of Carlo the First. Certainly, a final journey to the East awaits him—to Japan, to be precise. It's in Edo that he receives 'the precious teaching,' which leads him, as it seems, to turn his back on the world, choosing a kind of monastic existence. But one night in August of 1974, in his house in Chia, in the province of Viterbo, Pasolini dreamed a 'Descent Into Hell,' in which Carlo the First, now become a 'saint,' goes in search of his double. At a certain point in this dream, and the part of the work that would be derived from it, a centaur appeared, 'with the enormous dick between his front legs rather than his hind legs.'

I said before that I had had no relationship with the Madwoman after my stormy dismissal without notice from the Pasolini Foundation. In a sense, that's not completely true. Laura had already died—in 2004—when, one scorching summer afternoon, I took refuge in a multiplex cinema to take advantage of the air-conditioning and enjoy a final-cut version of *The Exorcist*. It had been many years since I'd seen William Friedkin's film, but memory hadn't deceived me: it's a real masterpiece, a milestone of cinematic art, one of those you can count on your fingers. What I had forgotten, though, is that some brilliant director of dubbing had decided to assign to the Madwoman the voice of the devil who takes possession of the child. The whole film is in this simple and incredibly effective invention, the contrast between the voice of the devil, in which all the horrors of the world seem to meet, and the heartbreaking sweetness of the eyes, the features of the child in whom he has taken up residence. Apart from some small effects of minor importance, almost all the supernatural in *The Exorcist* is concentrated in the fact that Evil speaks, doesn't stop speaking, displays its essence by revealing the sound of its voice as the most obscene and terrifying of its attributes. The voice is the vehicle of the evil spell and at the same time the evil spell itself, its sharpest and deadliest point. The artistic responsibility of the off-screen actor who plays the devil, in this case, both in the original and in the Italian version or any other version, is enormous. Michel de Certeau, the great Jesuit historian and philosopher, who was very interested in *The Exorcist* and other films of possession made in the seventies, wrote that the language of the possessed child is 'an *utterance* without *what is uttered*.' It's the paradox embodied by the act of speaking, 'where neither words nor terms exist any longer to say *what* takes possession of the subject.' Who better than Laura was able to give shape to this disturbing and tragic portent? How many times had she herself, shouting, hissing insults, laughing, been the pure vehicle of an evil that, pretending to say something, merely affirmed her presence, her utterance without what is uttered? With that catarrhal, bilious timbre of hers, evoking the eruption of a dark, infernal magma, the Madwoman adds to Friedkin's film a stunning baroque game. She matches the voice of the devil with a total immersion in the character, and at the same time laughs at her game, coloring with the light patina of a Bolognese accent certain wittier passages, certain interjections. Just as children do when they joke with their younger siblings in the dark, and frighten themselves with their own game. The devil possesses, in the film, and the child is possessed. Between them is the tense cord of a voice. And in it, in the heart of a sound that is the very heart of the drama, both poles of this magnetic field, of this relationship of force, this bond of violence, or more precisely of violent Eros, must remain active. It has to be, in other words, the voice both of possession and, at the same time, of being possessed: the childish joy of the rape, and the horror of one who, impotent, hears the enemy's triumph echoing in his own voice. The essence of the diabolic, ultimately, resides in just this sort of realm of uncertainty, in this sonorous mixing of the internal and the external, the self and the world that Laura, in her dubbing, expresses like the symptom of an evil from which she, when the film is over and the story forgotten, has not been able, poor Bolognese devil, to free herself.

'The bomb,' we read in the last group of notes of the type-script of *Petrolio*, 'is placed at the station in Bologna.' The idea is repeated in the last lines we have of *something writ-ten*, after a list of 'names of the Fascist deities,' diabolical characters who, at the moment of the bombing, 'divert the police at the Bologna station.' A little above, Pasolini had written that death 'as oblivion and loss of self has archaic and benign characteristics.' In that case, in effect, 'the tragedy is pure.'

'The tragedy is pure.'

SV SAGGI VALLECCHI

DI NOLA

ANTROPOLOGIA
RELIGIOSA

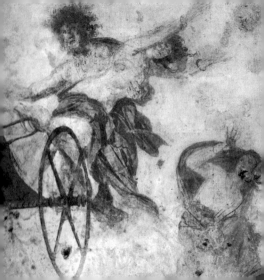

A Télestérion de Solon

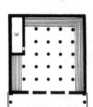

B de Pisistrate

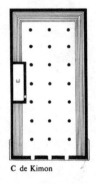

C de Kimon

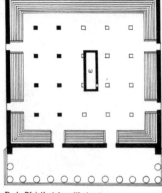

D de Périclès (plan d'Ictinos)

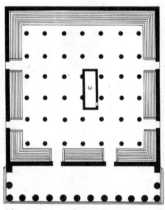

E Après la mort de Périclès - Romain (Koroibos, Métagénès, Xénoclès)

0   10   20   30   40M

' ... Like a flash of lightning'

I had my vision

VIRGINIA WOOLF, *To the Lighthouse*

Athens, Hotel Dryades, June 3, 2011, nine in the morning, Saturday. At the top of the hill that looms behind the hotel there is a small wood crisscrossed by stone paths, perennially occupied by drug addicts and melancholy, solitary women with dogs, widowed or abandoned, it's not clear. The truth is that one never understands anything clearly, and even less when we are touring: we observe, make our deductions, and the world passes by like an enigma, or, worse, as if there were no need to create enigmas, since there is nothing that has meaning. No children, anyway, in the park on the little hill, thick with lime trees. Immense swarms of tiny gnats suggest something unhealthy, corrupt, as in the gardens of Asia. Tonight there must have been a rave, or something like that—my sleep punctuated and hammered by an unchanging rhythm, by an electronic trance, not at all unpleasant. And the voices of the kids, in the alley outside my room on the second floor. While I was trying to get back to sleep, when the light of dawn had already appeared, I thought that there must exist in me, as in everyone, a better part, a *point in the soul*, maybe nothing other than a reserve of restlessness, the most invaluable of reserves: the possibility of imagining myself a pilgrim, a seeker of signs, someone who moves in the world (even when the world appears opaque, hostile, impenetrable) as if he were spurred by an absence, by an emptiness, as if he had lost something very important and precious—*not remembering, however, what it is.*

During the day, this third of June, the blaze of the sun will be powerful, will make you sweat, but not as in July and August, when around here—Athens and its environs—it often mixes with a thick luminous fog, the color of ivory, forming a murderous compound of heat and humidity. I have the numbers of the two buses that go to Eleusis, A16 and B16, noted in the back of the book—they seem like the names of vitamins, or of rockets ready to raze to the ground unsuspecting cities, reducing them to heaps of rubble teetering on the edge of enormous craters. The square that the buses leave from is anonymous, immense, and extraordinarily silent, as if a magical ban separated it from the noise of Athens. It has an official name and a name by which everyone knows it and insists on calling it, and is so without notable features, so similar to thousands of other spacious squares in southern Europe, that even if you're sure it's the first time you've been here, you look at it as things are looked at in the mirror of memory: simultaneously intimate and remote.

'Of all the divine things that exist among men,' writes a certain Aelius Aristides in the second century after Christ, 'Eleusis is the most awesome and the most luminous. In what place on earth has news so marvelous ever been proclaimed, have the sacred rites aroused greater awe, has a greater contrast ever existed between the seen and the heard?' It's not clear what this conflict between the two most powerful senses, sight and hearing, consisted of, which sank like a knife into the soft and inert material of habits—surprise and revelation.

In essence, the road from Athens to Eleusis is a long straight avenue, which crosses the periphery of the city and cuts through the plain to the arm of the sea between the island of Salamis and the mainland. A median strip divides the two directions of traffic, both hopelessly jammed, like a punishment of the hereafter, an eternal punishment. Lining the road, without interruption, are car and motorcycle dealers, small bank branches, barred warehouses, stores selling paint, wood, electrical equipment and materials, hairdressers and beauty salons with an equivocal look, post offices, travel agencies with the logos of the biggest ferry and hydrofoil companies, supermarkets with bargain prices, real-estate agents, sheds for seeds and grains, nurseries with displays of garden décor—a triumph of plaster reproductions of famous classical statues. Nothing in the world renders the idea of infinity more acutely than this succession of low buildings—a straight Mayan road decorated with banners, crowded with signs, sordid and hyperbolic. Every hundred meters a blue-and-white billboard reassures those who always feel lost, who live in constant fear of having taken the wrong road, of having gotten on the wrong bus: ELEFSINA, it says, this is the road to Eleusis. The old road must have had quite a different route, it certainly wasn't so wide; maybe it connected the small towns scattered over the great plain.

Everything departed from Athens, and proceeded toward Eleusis, even in the time of the Mysteries. But this departure, which was the solemn start of the celebrations, was conceived as a return. Dig deeply into a thing that really has some importance, some potent, not counterfeit, reality, and sooner or later you'll find inside it its contrary, its opposite and complementary pole. The woman lying hidden in the man and hatred in love, the return disguised as departure. In fact on the nineteenth of the month of Boedromion (a little after the middle of September), the *iera*, the sacred objects that a few days earlier had made the journey from Eleusis to Athens, returned, accompanied by an excited crowd of thousands of men and women, stunned by fasting and the weariness of the journey. It took an entire day to cover the route that the bus takes, in spite of the traffic, in forty minutes. Arriving at the bridge over the Ilisos, the small river that cuts the plain in two, the procession hurled a series of insults addressed to the most important Athenians—people who on no other occasion would it have been possible to address with such impunity. These ritual insults, or *gefirismi,* have an air of Carnival, of the World Upside Down that is like the first stage of the complete subversion of reality and its meanings implicit in the initiation procession.

At Eleusis Demeter was worshipped in consideration of her connection to the Daughter, Persephone, and the gifts made to humanity: the cultivation of grain and the Mysteries themselves. Eleusis, in its essence, is the sanctuary of the Two Goddesses, Mother and Daughter. The first wandering desperately from land to land, inconsolable for the loss of the other, kidnapped by Pluto. In the meantime Persephone has become the queen of the world of the dead, a divinity almost as powerful as her mother. But in Greece they have been talking about Demeter since times so remote that the stories about her are still saturated, in what we can glimpse, with a primeval violence and cruelty. In Arcadia her name was Erynis, the Fury, or Melaina, the Black: Poseidon had raped her after assuming the guise of a stallion. From the union were born Areion, the cursed horse, and a girl whose name can't be uttered—*arretos kore* Euripides calls her, alluding to ancient beliefs. A wooden statue portrays Demeter with the head of a mare, a dolphin in one hand and a dove in the other. All the dead ended up in the womb of this furious goddess, this raped black mare.

For Euripides Demeter is the 'mountain goddess,' the 'mother of the gods,' the great mother—so the chorus in *Helen* invokes her. Her grief at the loss of Persephone is not an ordinary grief, it strikes the Cosmos, halting its action, decreeing its end, death by hunger and want.

Cesare Brandi in the *Corriere della Sera*, June 27, 1965: 'Eleusis is a desecrated place.' It can't be denied. Agents of desecration: the chimneys, first of all, that begin to appear when the bus, reaching the sea, turns north, in a landscape of factories, construction sites, shipyards. In the hot months, the industrial fumes mix with exhaust gases, the haze, the dust—and everything fades into a blur, trembles in its own desolation. And yet, Brandi observes, in an instant the spring is released—and 'the machinery of an age-old spell is again in motion.' In two deep furrows dug into a stone floor, for example, the illusion of a sound, 'the creaking of the bronze door,' is still concealed.

This bus, A16 or B16, runs up and down on one of those routes on the periphery that are traveled at all hours, in all the cities of the world, by poor people or people of a level just above, small spruced-up shopkeepers, like those two Indians opposite me, young, perhaps related in some way, or only by some prosaic, laborious business matter—a garage, a small supermarket. And then there is a shepherd, a notable exemplar, a shepherd as someone might draw him in a comic strip, with a big reddish handkerchief around his neck, worn boots, vest over his checked shirt. He must have gone to Athens to pay insurance, to settle something in an office or in the family. Maybe he took advantage of it for a quickie at the house of an old prostitute. Certainly he is returning: as soon as he could, he got on the bus, Athens he doesn't like at all. He gives off a faint but insistent odor of sweat, which spreads through the bus when the driver brakes and the air no longer comes in through the open windows. After crossing an area dominated by big cranes and other naval shipyard equipment, we turn onto a narrower street, IERA ODOS, the Sacred Way, up to the first intersection. There are knots of people waiting at the bus stops; old people walking without evident purpose; a kiosk selling cigarettes and drinks; a bank open on the other side of the street. The Sacred Way continues amid the traffic for a few blocks, then becomes a pedestrian way, hopelessly pretentious, flanked by oleander bushes and stunted saplings, and emerges— after meeting a horrible modern statue of Aeschylus, the local pride—in a small deserted square, where an empty, unused merry-go-round, with its little boats and ponies, is abandoned to itself, immobile and forgotten for eternity. From there you cross the street in the direction of a low hill;

you go alongside an enclosure up to a gate beside which is a booth that sells entrance tickets to the excavations. In the whole area of the so-called Propylaea, from the Roman era, the first that you pass through as you proceed toward the cave at the base of the hill, or even higher up, big dogs, without collars, survey your passage. A bitch that has just given birth, as the guard explains to us, growls and shows her teeth, because she's hidden her young somewhere in the ruins, at the edge of the vast entrance square, maybe behind the bust of the Emperor Antoninus Pius.

If the charge of having revealed something about the Eleusinian Mysteries was proved true, it brought death, or at a minimum exile. Outside the moment of the ceremony reserved for the priests and the initiates, *one was not supposed to speak about it at all*; this was the forbidden. On the basis of the works that remain, it's hard to say in what way Aeschylus was marked by a crime so grave, even graver if one considers that he was also born in Eleusis, and to betray the chain of the secret of the Mysteries for him must have meant, in some way, to betray also his homeland, his origins. Aristotle, who tells this story, wishes to absolve Aeschylus, suggesting that it was a mistake made thoughtlessly, without bad intentions, that the great tragic poet didn't know that the things he said were in fact not to be said, *aporreta*. Maybe Aristotle is right, or maybe, on the other hand, Aeschylus acted with malice: we'll never know. But the story of Aeschylus immediately brought to mind P.P.P. In his case, too, one could formulate a charge that he revealed Mysteries: his fundamental attitude when he writes *Petrolio* is to make public a secret rite, a Mystery, desecrating it, making it into a literary work. Beyond their individual fates, in short, Aeschylus and P.P.P. seem united by a slightly equivocal air, of people who have made a mistake, irreparably, provoking a dangerous and powerful caste of priests, of policemen, of guardians of who knows what. That was how P.P.P. imagined himself in the last years of his life. Someone who has leaked a secret.

Besides the story of Aeschylus, who had perhaps committed the sacrilege unwittingly, another story circulated, in which the evil intent can't be doubted, because it was a true profanation: at the home of a man named Polytion, a parody of the Mysteries was organized, like the Black Masses of the French libertines, many centuries later, in certain houses of ill repute near Paris. But here, too, as in the case of Aeschylus, the name involved in the scandal makes an impression, because it seems that among the sacrilegious was the great Alcibiades ('Some people,' writes the prudent Pausanias, 'who were certainly not the most obscure in Athens').

Desecrated or not, full of wild dogs or not, this is one of the most sacred places on earth, and the power of the sacred is still active and perceptible after so many centuries, like the radiation from an ancient nuclear disaster. It's here that the marvel that is initiation took place, near a hill hollowed out by a cave, which brings to mind a cliff looming over the sea. Plutarch doesn't know how to define the experience of initiation except by comparing it to what happens at the moment of death, when the soul, freed from the body, can return to enjoy true 'knowledge.' There is no better example than this, initiation and death are almost the same thing, a journey of the soul, a *psychic journey*, which begins in fear and bewilderment but proceeds toward a light. Plutarch's story is splendid, worthy of an Egyptian priest, or a Tibetan monk—'At first one wanders wearily, lost, running fearfully through the shadows without reaching any goal; then, before the end, one is invaded by every type of terror, fear, trembling, sweat, and anguish.' But this is only a transitory state. 'Finally a marvelous light pours in and one is welcomed into pure regions and meadows with dances and echoing voices, where the majesty of holy hymns is heard and sacred visions appear.' Once one has become 'free,' Plutarch continues, one observes from a distance the mass of the 'uninitiated,' of the 'unpurified,' who are still writhing in the mud of error and fear.

If Plutarch found no better term of comparison for initiation than the departure of the soul from the body at the moment of death, for Aristotle initiation is the model of something equally supreme, the ultimate goal of thought, the terminal vision of knowledge. This vision 'passes through the soul like a flash of lightning,' and can't be taught, because teaching is based on listening, it assaults hearing, while initiation acts directly on the mind, it leaves not a teaching but 'an imprint':

' ... *it passes through the soul like a flash of lightning* ... '

Instead of penetrating into the heart of the sanctuary right away, you can take the outer road and follow the walls, proceeding southward. The walls and the ramparts are surrounded by thick tall grass, which turns yellow with the arrival of summer. Beyond the fields, beyond the metal fence that marks the boundary of the whole area of the excavations, the traffic visible along a road on the periphery seems particularly distant and unreal, making no sound that can compete with the cry of the cicadas. At a certain point the mighty wall constructed by Lycurgus turns toward the top of the hill. On this side, the ascent is very gentle, and after a few dozen meters you are in the shadow of a square tower, and a smaller door allows access to the sanctuary from the southwest. From this entrance you can have a first view of the area of the Telesterion, the sacred heart of Eleusis, at the foot of the hill, which is steeper on that side. Up here is where the museum was built, a little apart; it's a rectangular structure, with three large rooms opening onto a terrace, where, among all the various artifacts, there is a small, very moving statue of the two goddesses: the heads are missing, but it's them, the Daughter sitting in her Mother's arms. It's the triumph of Demeter, who has found Persephone, returned for a time to the light of the sun, among the living—but the sculptor brilliantly rendered this mythical event in a familiar, very natural pose, expressing the almost animal satisfaction of the two bodies finally reunited. We must consider that the Daughter's pose is one that we would expect of a child, whereas she is a woman, a wife, the queen of the Underworld, at least as tall as her mother. But the body has its memory, and, sitting on her mother's lap, the adult woman recovers something of her childhood; the bond between the two goddesses recedes in time to a happy vanished past. It's as if the renunciation of majesty, to appear in a form so mortal—the child and its mamma—were a step carefully calculated by the two Goddesses, a confirmation and not a diminishment of their power. It's an opening to the most effective of spells: identification.

In spite of the imprudent Aeschylus and the blasphemous Alcibiades, in spite of all the poisonous gossip of the Christian writers, the most astonishing and disconcerting fact of Eleusis is that, ultimately, we know nothing of the content of the supreme vision, and therefore of the ultimate meaning of initiation. That means that in the course of many centuries multitudes of Athenians and foreigners were initiated, without the secret ever being divulged. How is that possible? Fear of punishment must have counted, but it doesn't seem a very effective deterrent. The only explanation: the primacy of the experience over any possible account. The vision wasn't translatable into words. You had to be there, while the hierophant, the high priest, invoking the Girl seized in the kingdom of the dead, beat the *echeion*, a kind of large gong, not very different from the one that was used in the theater to imitate thunder. You had to have performed all the rites, observed all the customs, starting with the journey from Athens to Eleusis, and then the sacrifice of the pig, the ultimate Mystery animal, in honor of Eubuleus, the swineherd who, involuntary witness to the kidnapping of Persephone, was hurled into the chasm by Pluto's chariot—hurled unaware, one might say, in mythology, as one might be hurled into a hole. At the Archeological Museum in Athens there are three heads of this sublime zombie who has emerged from the Underworld, with his thick curly locks, his perfect features hiding the deep black shadow that has possessed his entire person and looks out from the hollow eye sockets.

The cave, at the foot of the hill at Eleusis, is a kind of memorial, representing the chasm created by Pluto so that he can reach his underground kingdom, with Persephone, who has just been captured, struggling in his arms. This cave is the only monument in the entire sanctuary that has remained intact over the centuries. Everything around it was destroyed, is a mass of rubble, but the cave is there, the most enduring symbol. This morning someone placed a bouquet of flowers at the entrance, as a gesture of affection, a souvenir left by a living person on the threshold of the world of the dead. Surely there is no place more venerable than these sacred grottoes, dug into the rock in imitation of the gates to the hereafter.

Pausanias, the curious Pausanias, who knows every temple, every portico, every statue in all Greece, and willingly expatiates on the most minute details, having, so to speak, stuck his nose in everywhere and picked up all the information there was to pick up, is very careful not to let out half a word too many about Eleusis. I was detained by a vision, he confesses at one point, just as I was preparing to go too far with the subject. And also: 'A dream kept me from describing what one found inside the ruins of the sanctuary.'

But what happened? What is it that Pausanias, warned by his dream, wasn't supposed to reveal? What we know for sure is that, a short distance from the cave dug into the hillside, there existed a heart of the sanctuary, the place where the initiation produced the final vision, the one that could change an individual's fate forever, both during life and after death. Of this structure, the Telesterion, there remains only the floor and a part of a side wall that backs onto the hill. In the course of the centuries, from the age of Solon to the Romans, the Telesterion was reconstructed and enlarged so many times that if you look at the plans of the archeologists one after another what comes to mind is the development of an organism, starting from the embryo. At the end, when the building reached its adult form, one crossed the portico and entered a grand hall surrounded by a tier of steps against the walls. The roof was held up by dozens of columns, and the effect was of entering a real forest of stone, within which a smaller space was hidden, a room enclosed on all sides, apart from a narrow entrance door. Maybe it wasn't even a space bounded by walls, maybe some wood or fabrics were enough to separate it from the rest. In any case, that was the center of the center, the place of the vision and of the reawakening—and therefore, without a shadow of a doubt, the truest place it was possible to conceive of, the nest and the shelter itself, so to speak, of the supreme level of reality.

As Aristotle says: this ultimate knowledge is a flash of lightning. There are no roads that lead there; there is, rather, a leap, exactly as if one were left to go into the darkness, into death. That happened at the right moment, when to the weariness caused by the walk and the fasting was added the intoxication of the kykeon, the sacred drink, the vehicle of communion with the goddesses.

The crowns of myrtle (the plant most beloved of the gods of the underworld), the torches, the containers of sacred objects, the ritual formulas: all that which has been daringly handed down to us is a pile of incomprehensible fragments, tiny shards from which it's impossible to recreate the shape of the smashed vase. Certain Christian authors, who were not initiates and had never seen anything, thought of a kind of Mystery play, a sacred representation. The subject of that initiation drama would have been the rape of Persephone, or the coupling of Zeus and Demeter. All that is unlikely. But in one of the most inspired pages of *The Birth of Tragedy*, Nietzsche writes that the scene of the drama, and the action that unfolds there, has to be thought of 'ultimately and originally only as a *vision*.' And this vision is produced by the chorus, which is '*a chorus of the transformed*,' and therefore of initiates. The members of this chorus, Nietzsche writes, 'have become timeless servants of their god, living outside every social sphere.'

Another important element must have been the *kernos*, a terracotta vase that contained some small vessels—little bowls joined to one another, containing *horminum* leaves, poppy heads, grain and barley, peas, grains of vetches, lentils, favas, grains of spelt, barley, preserved fruit, honey, oil, wine, milk, unwashed sheep's wool.

Probably, the various receptacles that held the sacred objects were involved in some type of ritual of handling, as it seems from a formula that might have been uttered before entering the sanctuary—'*I have fasted and have drunk kykeon: I've taken from the basket and put back in the bin; I've taken it again and moved it into the case.*' But what was taken, and moved, from the basket to the bin and from the bin to the case? Images of the genital organs? The symbols of the

Goddesses—the stalk of grain and the pomegranate? At a certain point, turned toward the sky, the faithful shouted 'Rain' and then, lowering their gaze to the earth, added: 'Be pregnant.'

The height of the vision: it might be a single object, a symbol capable of sustaining the whole story of the two Goddesses, the Mother and the Daughter, ferrying the initiate, so to speak, from the old life to the new, from the shadows of ignorance to that state of blessedness that coincides with true knowledge. According to the malevolent, slandering Tertullian, the object that was shown at the supreme moment was a phallus, a symbol of the male member, '*simulacrum membri virilis revelatur.*' Unlikely that it really went like that; the display of a harvested grain stalk, of which another Christian writer, Hippolytus, speaks, in his *Refutation of All Heresies*, seems more likely.

' ... it passes through the soul like a flash of lightning ... '

Like Aristotle, Plato, too, recognizes in the vision of the initiation the absolute, unachievable model of all other knowledge. The only state more perfect than the initiation of Eleusis, he writes in the Phaedrus, is the condition of the soul before the catastrophe of birth and the fall into time, into matter, into what we call the body in which 'we are imprisoned like an oyster in its shell.' The light was pure and brilliant, and we ourselves were also pure. Beauty was ours to see in all its brightness, and we were 'whole and perfect and unacquainted with the evils that waited for us,' once we were born.

' ... it passes through the soul like a flash of lightning ... '

Like a flash.

Like
  A
    Flash.

[Eleusis-Athens, June 2011.]

NOTES

1. As all those who were acquainted with Laura Betti know, the only male who was spared a feminine declension was Pasolini. In the fine documentary made by Paolo Petrucci, titled *The Passion of Laura*, Francesca Archibugi—one of the last to direct her in a film—has interesting things to say about Betti's verbal inventiveness. In her opinion, the prototype of that incessant transmutation from male to female was a word that she repeated often—*la cazza* (rather than *il cazzo*, the penis). To what type of mental image, Francesca Archibugi asks, justly, can a word like *la cazza* correspond? By the way, *La cazza* would be a splendid title for a book or a film.

2. Apart from the sad circumstances that transformed it into a kind of farewell, the interview has a rare beauty and power, as Fabrizio Gifuni showed in 2004, bringing it to the stage in a piece entitled *'Na specie di cadavere lunghissimo* (A kind of very long corpse). I would also like to point out here that in 1995 Michele Gulinucci published an outstanding selection of interviews with Pasolini from 1955 to 1975.

3. The best example of this capacity for contagion is Antonin Artaud; the subject is examined in a book by Sylvère

Lotringer, *Mad Like Artaud*. I recommend this brilliant work (which has also been staged) to anyone interested in the tremendous subject of the *influence* that human beings (*certain* human beings, like Artaud and P.P.P.) exert over their fellow-man. 'All those who have anything to do with Artaud are paranoid,' Paule Thévenin, the friend and confidante of Artaud in his last years, and the editor of his *Collected Works,* declares to the author at one point. Certainly there would be no lack of material for anyone who wanted to write a *Mad Like Pasolini* inspired by the French example.

4. 'The creative act,' Marina Tsvetaeva wrote in her stupendous portrait of the painter Natalia Goncharova, 'is distinguished from the Creator because, the first day follows immediately after the sixth, again the first. To us here on earth no seventh day is granted; it is granted perhaps to our things, not to us.' (*Natalia Goncharova. Vita e creazione,* edited by Luciana Montagni, Einaudi, Turin, 1995.)

5. It's hard for me to believe that Pasolini did not take into account, during the years of *Petrolio,* the great essay by Mircea Eliade (written in 1958) on androgyny and the 'mystery of totality.' Throughout innumerable esoteric traditions, Eliade explains, with his usual abundance of provocative citations, androgyny represents the high point of initiation and the 'spiritual perfection' needed for true knowledge. There is a detail in *Petrolio* that could be explained only by recourse to information found in Eliade's essay, collected in a book entitled *Mephistopheles and the Androgyne.* In Note 17, at the end of a series of astonishing erotic adventures

undertaken in Turin, Carlo the Second has a complicated prophetic vision, in which he is bound hand and foot to a wheel suspended in the void. First he sees a 'savage woman,' endowed, however, with 'an enormous penis.' Next to her is a man, so small that it takes Carlo some time to notice him. This man has a completely normal penis, but in his groin Carlo sees 'a long cut, a deep black wound,' which he himself holds 'slightly spread with his fingers.' Carlo has no doubt: that wound 'was the vulva.' The man who carries in his body both sexes is not only an oneiric fantasy but a precise allusion to a rite of passage among the Australian aborigines, who practice on the body of novices what Eliade describes as 'initiatory sub-incisions': wounds that symbolize the vagina. All the rites and legends connected to androgyny are subject to a single traditional belief, according to which 'one cannot be something perfectly if one is not also, simultaneously, its opposite.'

6. Someone will surely remember that it is precisely the 'state of exception,' according to the jurist Carl Schmitt, which is the supreme prerogative of dictatorships. It is the tyrant who proclaims the state of exception. What is valid for states, one might say, is valid also for comparatively small human communities, like families and workplaces.

7. An extreme example of this will to power disguised by its opposite is *The Idiots*, Lars von Trier's masterpiece. If I may indulge for a moment in such groundless conjectures, I think that Pasolini would have appreciated the Danish director's results, without giving any value to the aesthetic theory that is its premise (the so-called Dogma 95, which

to many people, including me, at first seemed to represent some kind of aesthetic revolution, but which today seems a small thing, one of the many bubbles in the glass of the fizzy nineteen-nineties).

8. Andrea Zanzotto has written a lot about Pasolini, but in this note I'd like to recall a stupendous poem in dialect, published in 1986 in the collection entitled *Idioma*. Zanzotto, Pasolini's contemporary, imagines P.P.P. as a boy, waiting for the train to go to school, 'between Sacile and Conegliano,' just as he, Zanzotto, did, in the same region and in the same period, passing through the same little country stations with the bell that went '*ding ding ding*.' But ten kilometers, for boys at the time, was 'an immensity,' and so the two poets met only as adults. It's worth quoting the first lines of this poem, because one does not read such heartbreaking verses every day: 'You who were eating your piece of bread / on the way to school on the train / between Sacile and Conegliano; you weren't far from me but in those days / ten kilometers was an immensity.' Later, as adults, Zanzotto continues in this letter to a dead man, 'we read each other's work, we quarreled, we were different people, but as for what really matters we had the same idea' ('*de quel che val se 'véa l'istessa idea*').

9. 'As far as I know,' Pasolini confides to Quintavalle, 'even that myth about the Negro is unfounded. When I was in Nubia I searched high and low, and yet I didn't find one, a single one, that lived up to that reputation' (*Giornate di Sodoma, Days of Sodom*, pp. 33-34). We have to admit: this image of P.P.P. searching Nubia 'high and low' for exceptional measurements is really sublime.

10. Some time ago, walking along the Boulevard Saint-Germain in Paris, not far from the Café de Flore and on the same side of the street, I discovered a plaque, attached to the façade of a small, elegant eighteenth-century house, informing passersby that there, for years, the Duc de Saint-Simon distilled the poisons of his *Memoirs*. Long live slander! Long live bloody gossip! Anyone who does not understand its subtle and profound poetry is not worthy of practicing the *humanities*, which, having by definition man as their subject, cannot hide his wretchedness, treacherousness, incurable foolishness, and infinite forms of absurdity. That small white house set among buildings of greater mass seemed to me a temple worthy of the same worship, if not more, as that reserved for the houses of lyric poets, philosophers, mystics.

11. The author has some very felicitous touches, which it would be a sin, given the difficulty of finding the book, not to mention. For example, when he recalls the scene where the prisoners are inspected to determine whether men's or women's asses are more beautiful. 'We contemplate vaginal lips of every shape and color,' Quintavalle writes, with an effective historical present, 'many with the thread of a Tampax hanging out, in competition with the hanging balls of the men' (*Days of Sodom*). And I would add the exact (and meager) balance sheet of the 'vile acts' of the film, which, ultimately, 'consisted of many acts of manual masturbation, some oral acts, some of sodomy, a lot of voyeurism of these acts, two big episodes of shit-eating and one where pee is drunk.' As for the photographs, I would point out that Quintavalle's book is enhanced by an insert of photographs

235

taken on the set by Deborah Beer, the wife of Gideon Bachmann, a scholar of cinema and a documentarian. Bachmann kept in his archive all the photographs that Beer took on the set of *Salò*. It's an exceptional document about the end of Pasolini's life, from which Giuseppe Bertolucci, in 2006, made an original and enlightening film, *Pasolini prossimo nostro* (*Pasolini Our Neighbor*).

12. It's very much to the point to quote the last two lines of Yeats's *Among School Children* (1927): 'O body swayed to music, o brightening glance / How can we know the dancer from the dance?' Indeed: How to distinguish the dancer from the dance? Yeats, it should be noted, is talking about innocent schoolchildren; we are speaking of the notorious P.P.P. But, apart from the fact (well known to Yeats) that no one is innocent, Pasolini could never be accused of calculation, of a lack of abandon.

13. The anecdote seems to me completely credible, because there was no reason to invent either the whole thing or the particular details. That '*something written*,' even for just a few hours, had in P.P.P.'s mind the title *Armadio* can't be more than a little surprising, given the compositional method. The first to forget about it must have been the author himself.

14. 'A modern *Satyricon*,' P.P.P. writes—thus suggesting that the author is a new Petronius, besides a new Sade. The *Satyricon*, like the *120 Days of Sodom* and like *Petrolio*, is a long fragment, in which parts that are well-shaped and complete alternate with simple notes that have no

development. Petronius and P.P.P., among other things, can provide material for an interesting exercise in psychological comparison. Tacitus provides a portrait of Petronius which gives us something to think about (*Annals XVI*, 18-19). Like P.P.P., Petronius sleeps late, one of those men who seem to live their true life more at night than during the day. He loves 'refined luxury' but is not a wastrel. At the moment of assuming public office (proconsul in Bithynia, consul in Rome), however, as the severe Tacitus, who never jokes about these things, testifies, this man of the world 'showed himself to be rigorous and equal to his duties.' When this period passed, he fell back into dissipation, or, rather, as Tacitus observes, with an extraordinary acuity, into the 'imitation of vices'—'*revolutus ad vitia seu vitiorum imitatione*'—which is a perpetual characteristic of the novelist, who, in part, is a person 'well informed about the facts' and in part pretends, draws back, knows just what to describe and what instead one must give up in order not to succumb. At a certain point in life this difficult equilibrium is no longer practical—it's as if P.P.P. were progressively swallowed up by the night, and vices, to put it as Tacitus does, were no longer the object of 'imitation' at a safe distance.

15. Modenese by birth, and professor of Romance philology at the University of Rome, Aurelio Roncaglia was a very intelligent man, whose erudition was boundless. Pasolini might have asked him more than one piece of advice about the false 'incompleteness' of *Petrolio*. Anyway, there was an affection between the two of them that apparently was not damaged by the rather unkind caricature that P.P.P. has of the professor in *The Divine Mimesis*: 'A Romance

philologist, trim and with his head shaved like a lieutenant in the Engineer Corps.' It should be noted that Roncaglia is taking part in a lighthearted conversation with other important intellectuals in the living room of Casa Bellonci, headquarters of the already notorious Strega Prize. But the friendship between the two does not seem to have been harmed by this innocent needling. As I was saying, Roncaglia was a very intelligent man. He loved painstaking historical research, which required a well-developed sense of detail, like a detective's. He never wanted to publish real books, apart from two obscure grammars, of ancient French and Provençale. 'Philology,' he often said, 'is a frittata of obvious solutions.' I was in time to attend a university course taught by Roncaglia, shortly before he retired. He lectured in the biggest classroom, a vast amphitheater where, in the ten preceding years, all sorts of things had happened. Roncaglia explained the secrets of the *Chanson de Roland*, writing on the blackboard the most important names and dates of Norman history, finding room, with his piece of chalk, between the enormous letters of a slogan in yellow paint: 'Homage to Tristan Tzara.' The twentieth century really was marvelous. I consider myself lucky to have been there, to have observed some of its last fires.

16. All the materials used by P.P.P. in the work on *Petrolio* are in a file at the Gabinetto Vieusseux, in Florence. It's a moderate-size collection of photocopies and newspaper clippings that has been systematically studied by Iolanda Romualdi, a student of Walter Siti's. Many of the results of Romualdi's thesis, which is hard to find, were used by Silvia De Laude in her commentary on *Petrolio*, published in 2005

in the Mondadori Oscars. There are no excuses, then: this commentary certainly isn't perfect, but it should make all the 'conspiracy theorists' reflect on Pasolini's method of proceeding. But of course the love for theses is even blinder than carnal love, or, if you prefer, platonic love ...

17. As we know, the major suspicions are now concentrated on Note 21, of which the typescript of *Petrolio*, in its current state, has preserved only the title: *Flashes of light on Eni*. It's very enticing for those who think that Pasolini's final work consisted in revealing the secrets of Italian oil politics, the death of Mattei, etc. I will summarize the affair for those who have missed this small but significant slice of Italian literary life. Among the newspaper articles that dealt with it I would recommend looking up, for balance and expertise, the one published by Paolo Di Stefano in the *Corriere della Sera*, March 12, 2010 (*Petrolio, il mistero in mostra* [the mystery on display]). In the spring of 2010, on the occasion of an important antiquarian book show in Milan, the existence of this vanished chapter was made known. The principals of the affair, whose behavior is somewhere between shifty and sly, seem to have emerged from the very pages of *Petrolio*: the not infrequent case of life imitating art, as the divine Oscar Wilde put it. The so-called 'owners' of the valuable unpublished fragment remained in the shadows—which was understandable, since the material, if it actually existed, was stolen from Pasolini, and so would have to be given back to the family, once the proper police investigations had taken place. To this should be added the fact that the shocking announcement of the discovery was made by Senator Marcello Dell'Utri, a genuine Palermitan

and extremely loyal lieutenant of Silvio Berlusconi since the eighties, who was sentenced in June of the same year to seven years in prison for complicity in a Mafia association, having already negotiated a sentence of two years and three months for tax fraud. One may think what one likes of Senator Dell'Utri, a cultivated reader, lover of the theater, publisher of classics, collector of rare books. To many he is a scoundrel who should die behind bars, to others a martyr, innocent victim of a prejudiced system. But one thing readers of *Petrolio* can't deny: the fact that it was precisely a person of that type who announced the reappearance of the unpublished chapter of *Petrolio* is a fact that seems invented, it's so perfect, and must have delighted the ironic soul of P.P.P., wherever it might have been in the spring of 2010. Completing the farce with a fitting last act, the criminals who had the precious stolen fragment, if they ever existed, smelled the police and were heard from no more. They couldn't do otherwise. If the material had been genuine, they would have had to explain how they came into possession of it; if it was fake, they would have had to answer for the fraud. The sublime Dell'Utri remained, the only one who had had (according to him) the chapter in hand and could at least provide a description. No, he hadn't had time to read it. It was about ten sheets of copy paper, typed, with corrections in pen. Maybe because of a typing mistake, the chapter was titled *Lampi su Eni* and not *sull'Eni*, as it is on the published page. It's the title more than anything else that makes me suspicious about the authenticity of this lost chapter, because Pasolini writes the title of a chapter and then starts the text below, leaving at most two or three white lines between the title and the text. And then, here and there in *Petrolio*, there are blank pages, which show only the titles of chapters that haven't been written. Maybe because Pasolini didn't have time to write them, and had put those titles as reminders, maybe because, in doing that, the writer intended to give the whole that aspect of incompleteness which he had decided on from the start. The fact is that, besides the blank page that contains only the title *Flashes of light on Eni*, there are others in the typescript that are exactly the same: for example (it's Note 42) *The story of xxx and xxx and their three children xxx*, or *Young prick (The story of Tonino)*, or, again, *The Negro and the Redhead* (Notes 52 and 52b). And on the other hand Pasolini never writes the title on a blank page and starts the chapter on the next, making what typographers call a half title. On the other hand, these purely philological considerations are not unambiguous. It's always true as well that these Italian stories, with their perpetual atmosphere of a criminal-like commedia dell'arte, present elements of the probable mixed in with the unlikely. Dell'Utri, for example, speaks of copy paper, which in fact was used by P.P.P., along with normal paper, while he was drafting the novel. And then there is the fact that there are big gaps in the numbering of the notes in this section of the book (there is a kind of jump from 23 to 30, as if in fact something were missing). But the most intriguing argument, for those who wish to maintain the existence of a vanished chapter, is a passage in Note 22a, where Pasolini refers the reader 'who wants to refresh his memory' to what he has already written in a preceding chapter, entitled *Flashes of light on Eni*. Even skeptics, faced with this plain statement, have to admit that the existence of the chapter is a possibility that has a certain likelihood. But not even this argument clinches it, if we think that Pasolini wanted to construct an incomplete, gap-filled text, of which various and contradictory versions exist. To refer the reader to an unwritten chapter could be a perfect mystifying trick. Two other very similar examples of reference to information already given before should be considered. The first example comes from Note 74: 'The house that Carlo had rented was, as we have seen, one of those run-down semi-legal houses on a street parallel to the main street of Quadraro, which ran along a railway line; beyond the railway rose the barrier of the seventeenth-century walls of the Mandrione.' We know that Carlo the Second, after the separation from his double, lives on the periphery, but, given the topographical precision, the 'as we have seen' seems definitely out of place. Still less ambiguous is the case of the opening words of Note 130: 'Often in Carlo's dreams (as we have said) a mute character appeared.' There is not the slightest mention of this type of recurrent dream in the whole text. In other words, both the skeptics and those who would like to believe in the story of the 'stolen chapter' have some cards to play. I confess I do not hold an unshakable idea on the subject. But may the reader who has followed me in these boring philological lucubrations forgive me: truth or falsehood, our judgment of the work would not change in the least. Because there is one thing that Pasolini's method makes us a hundred per cent sure of: even the vanished chapter devoted to Eni would have contained secondhand information, which could be found more or less easily in the press of the time.

18. Even odder, on the part of conspiracy-theorist readers,

is the absolute deafness to the literal meaning of many of Pasolini's statements, according to which, for example, the book (Note 6b) 'refers to nothing other than itself alone,' and should be considered 'a false transposition of reality.' And again in Note 37, which is the one titled *something written*, we read: 'I have chosen, for my self-sufficient and pointless construction, materials that are apparently meaningful.' And I omit other equally explicit passages.

19. I'm speaking of a human type that is widespread throughout the planet, wherever there are the comfortable social conditions that allow it to prosper. But I don't think that there is anyplace in the world like Rome, overflowing with idle and delightful existences. In certain neighborhoods in the center, where the tables of the cafés are crowded in the same way *at every hour of the day*, the concentration is such as to challenge every statistical probability.

20. Giuseppe Bertolucci, in a book of essays and reminiscences, included an old review of *Salò* by Cesare Musatti, published in the January-February 1976 issue of *Cinema Nuovo*. The dean of Italian psychoanalysis also addresses the lack of a real sexuality in the sadistic libertine—the eternal bad boy. Pasolini's last film 'doesn't present the death of sex,' Musatti writes, 'but rather a sex that is still unable to be born.' And also, with a truly remarkable subtlety: 'This immaturity is confirmed by the fact that the film has no conclusion, but only unsatisfied tension. The viewer, too, leaves the theater with a similar sense of emptiness. Along with sadness, because one cannot help linking that failure of sexuality to the death of the author.'

21. For what follows, I cite a valuable article by Guglielmo Ragozzino, the nephew of Corrado Ragozzino, published in *il manifesto* November 10, 2005. The reading of *Questo è Cefis*, which is very instructive and in its way entertaining, is made possible today with gratitude to the online magazine *Il primo amore*, which republished the entire text.

22. It's a historical structure, well known to experts in Roman architecture. An essential but precise description can be found in the *Guide rionali di Roma* (Neighborhood guides to Rome), file 18, *Rione VII-Regola*, edited by Carlo Pietrangeli, part II, pp. 40-42 (Fratelli Palombi Editori, Rome, 1984). With its large rusticated entranceway, flanked by two smaller doors, Palazzo Montoro is described in this authoritative guide, not without reason, as 'grandiose.' But there exists a gloomy, disquieting grandiosity, which always suggests melancholy thoughts. Stars, mountain peaks, and tangled oak branches, decorating the façade, are a reminder of the many noble families that have taken their turns and mingled behind its damp, thick walls.

23. In *Ali with the blue eyes* P.P.P. also uses *glande* as a feminine noun. Walter Siti and Silvia De Laude note it in their edition of *Romanzi e racconti* (Novels and stories), vol. II, p. 1973. But it's an isolated case.

24. Ah, twentieth century, how I miss you! One goes so far as to feel nostalgia even for types like that French idiot, compared with the desert we have today.

25. P.P.P. and Philip Dick: that could be a truly stimulating subject for an exercise in literary criticism less boring than the usual. In both these extraordinary men, who spent their lives giving shape to what came from the most hidden depths of their inner worlds, a high degree of clairvoyance should be recognized—which is a gift very different from predicting the future (in this capacity, among other things, the ideas of both are very disappointing). Even more significant is the fact that a similar horror and a similar anguish seem to be driving both. The horror is roused by power, in whatever form it manifests itself (and the Dick of books like *Ubik* is not inferior to P.P.P. in understanding that the cordial and tolerant face of power based on consumerism does not diminish at all its basically fascist authoritarian nature). The anguish is that of one who, aware of the failure early on, realizes that he is the *only one* to have understood so completely that things aren't right, and knows that no one will believe him, but can't stop raising the alarm.

26. By sheer coincidence, Pasolini reads and reviews the book, showing a great appreciation for the work of this very learned scholar, anthropologist, and historian of religions. Yet again, we are faced with the evidence: *Petrolio* is a powerful Vacuum Tank, able to transform into meaningful material anything its author finds at hand. We should recall that the use Pasolini makes of the cover of *Antropologia religiosa* was observed for the first time by Iolanda Romualdi, the student of Walter Siti and author of a controversial graduate thesis in the academic year 2004-2005 (*Per un'edizione annotata di 'Petrolio'*; For an annotated edition of *Petrolio*).

27. The match ended 4-0, Milan, coached by Fabio Capello. Daniele Massaro got two goals. Not that Cruijff's Barcelona was a team of novices: Guardiola, Romario, the great Hristo Stoichkov all played on it. But also favoring Milan, perhaps, was the scorching memory of the preceding final, lost to Olympique de Marseille, in spite of all the auspicious predictions.

28. Pasolini, introducing our hero into the salons of the Quirinal, commits some inaccuracies that seem anything but involuntary: as if he wished, by small modifications of reality, to create a kind of parallel reality. That's the only way I can explain, unless it's a real mistake, the date of July 2nd, rather than June 2nd, for the Festival of the Republic. But, whether June or July, in the summer of 1972 the president was not Giuseppe Saragat, as we read in *Petrolio*, but Giovanni Leone.

29. A similar case of a text that is voluntarily interrupted, just as the heroine discovers the key to the mystery, is the last, unforgettable page of Thomas Pynchon's *The Crying of Lot 49*, published in 1966. On this subject, I recommend to the reader an essay by Sandro Portelli, *Non illudersi di non sapere: note su 'The Crying of Lot 49,'* in AA.VV., *La dissoluzione onesta. Scritti su Thomas Pynchon* ('Don't Delude Yourself That You Don't Know: Notes on *The Crying of Lot 49,'* in *Honest Dissolution. Writings on Thomas Pynchon)*, edited by Giancarlo Alfano and Mattia Carratello, Cronopio, Naples, 2003. Portelli's observations are very perceptive: they seem applicable, with disconcerting precision, to Pasolini's last book. On the last page of *Crying*, the

protagonist has apparently reached the moment of the 'final and conclusive' revelation. 'Pynchon,' Portelli writes, 'brings the reader to the edge of this Annunciation and leaves him there, sitting comfortably but without comfort: neither the comfort of knowledge nor that of unknowability; without the certainty of knowing but also without the absolution of not knowing.' It's unlikely, if not impossible, that P.P.P. knew Pynchon's youthful masterpiece (the first Italian translation goes back to 1995). But aren't the most illuminating affinities of literary history perhaps those which appear between writers who do *not* know each other, even by name? In comparison, study of the so-called 'sources' produces results that are completely predictable and boring. Not coincidentally, it's one of the favorite pastimes of academics.

BIBLIOGRAPHY

The list that follows is not intended to provide a bibliography, however minimal, for work on Pier Paolo Pasolini or Greek religion; it includes only texts that were cited directly or used in some other way in the drafting of this book.

Roberto Andreotti and Federico de Melis, *Gli amici della Giaguara*, in *Alias*, September 4, 2004.

Apollonius of Rhodes, *Argonautica*.

Marco Belpoliti, *Pasolini in salsa piccante*. With eight photographs by Ugo Mulas, Guanda, Parma, 2010.

Carla Benedetti and Maria Antonietta Grignani, editors. *A partire da 'Petrolio.' Pasolini interroga la letteratura*, Longo, Ravenna, 1995.

Giuseppe Bertolucci, *Pasolini prossimo nostro*, Ripley's Home video, 2007.

Laura Betti, *Teta veleta*, Garzanti, Milan, 1979.

Gianni Borgna and Carlo Lucarelli, *Così morì Pasolini*, in *Micromega*, n. 6, 2005.

Cesare Brandi, *Viaggio nella Grecia antica* (1954), Bompiani, Milan, 2011.

André Breton, *Laura aimantée* (1962), in *Écrits sur l'art et autres textes*, edited by Marguerite Bonnet, Gallimard, Paris, 2008.

Norman O. Brown, *Love's Body* (1966).

Michel de Certeau, *La lanterna del diavolo: Cinema e possessione*, translated by Maria Elisabetta Craveri, Edizioni Medusa, Milan, 2002.

Giorgio Colli, *La sapienza greca*, Vol. I, Adelphi, Milan, 1977.

Leonardo Colombati, *Laura Betti*, in *La canzone italiana 1861-2011*, Mondadori, Milan, 2011.

Gianfranco Contini, *Testimonianza per Pier Paolo Pasolini* (1980), in *Ultimi esercizi ed elzevirî*, Einaudi, Turin, 1988.

Alfonso Di Nola, *Antropologia religiosa: Introduzione al problema e campioni di ricerca*, Vallecchi, Florence, 1974.

Mircea Eliade, *Méphistophélès et l'Androgyne*, Gallimard, Paris, 1962.

Sándor Ferenczi, *Thalassa: A Theory of Genitality* (1924).

Massimo Fusillo, *La Grecia secondo Pasolini. Mito e cinema*, 2nd ed. Carocci, Rome, 2007.

Massimo Fusillo, *L'altro e lo stesso. Teoria e storia del doppio*, La Nuova Italia, Florence, 1998.

Marco Tullio Giordana, *Pasolini: Un delitto italiano*, Mondadori, Milan, 1994.

Antonio Gnoli and Franco Volpi, *Il Dio degli acidi. Conversazioni con Albert Hofmann*, Bompiani, Milan, 2003.

Enzo Golino, *Tra lucciole e Palazzo: Il mito Pasolini dentro la realtà*, Sellerio, Palermo, 1995.

Károly Kérenyi, *Eleusis: Archetypal Image of Mother and Daughter*, Routledge & Kegan Paul, London, 1967.

Enzo Lippolis, *Mysteria: Archeologia e culto nel santuario di Demetra a Eleusi*, Bruno Mondadori, Milan, 2006.

Nico Naldini, *Breve vita di Pasolini*, 2nd ed. Guanda, Parma, 2009.

Friedrich Nietzsche, *The Birth of Tragedy* (1872).

Walter F. Otto, *The Meaning of the Eleusinian Mysteries* (1939), in *The Mysteries: Papers from the Eranos Yearbooks*, edited by Joseph Campbell (1955).

Pier Paolo Pasolini, *Teorema* (1968), in *Romanzi e racconti 1963-1975*, edited by Walter Siti and Silvia De Laude, Mondadori, Milan, 1998.

Pier Paolo Pasolini, *Necrologio di una certa Laura Betti* (1971), in *Romanzi e racconti 1963-1975*, ibid.

Pier Paolo Pasolini, *La Divina Mimesis* (1975), in *Romanzi e racconti 1963-1975*, ibid.

Pier Paolo Pasolini, *Descrizioni di descrizioni* (1979), in *Saggi sulla letteratura e sull'arte*, edited by Walter Siti e Silvia De Laude, Vol. 2, Mondadori, Milan, 1999.

Pier Paolo Pasolini, *Petrolio*, edited by Maria Careri and Graziella Chiarcossi, with a philological note by Aurelio Roncaglia, Einaudi, Turin, 1992.

Pier Paolo Pasolini, *Interviste corsare sulla politica e sulla vita*, edited by Michele Gulinucci, Liberal Libri, Florence, 1995.

Pier Paolo Pasolini, *Petrolio*, edited by Silvia De Laude, Mondadori, Milan, 2010.

Pier Paolo Pasolini: Fotografie di Dino Pedriali, Johan & Levi, Verona, 2011.

Guglielmo Ragozzino, *Cefis, Pasolini e mio zio Corrado*, in *il manifesto*, November 10, 2005.

Uberto Paolo Quintavalle, *Giornate di Sodoma: Ritratto di Pasolini e del suo ultimo film*, SugarCo, Milano, 1976.

Dario Sabbatucci, *Il misticismo eleusino*, in *Il mito: Guida storica e critica*, edited by Marcel Detienne, Laterza, Rome-Bari, 1975.

Donatien-Alphonse-François de Sade, *Les 120 journées de Sodom* (1785).

Paolo Scarpi, editor. *Le religioni dei misteri*, Vol. I, Fondazione Lorenzo Valla-Mondadori, Milan, 2002.

Petrolio. Un progetto di Mario Martone a partire da 'Petrolio' di Pier Paolo Pasolini, Cronopio, Naples, 2003.

Barth David Schwartz, *Pasolini Requiem* (1992).

Walter Siti, *Scuola di nudo*, Einaudi, Turin, 1994

Walter Siti, *La magnifica merce*, Einaudi, Turin, 2004.

Walter Siti, *Troppi paradisi*, Einaudi, Turin, 2006.

Walter Siti, *Il contagio*, Mondadori, Milan, 2008.

Walter Siti, *Autopsia dell'ossessione*, Mondadori, Milan, 2010.

Emanuele Trevi, *Laura Betti in Grecia*, in *Nuovi Argomenti*, Vol. 28, October-December 2004.

Emanuele Trevi, *Via Merulana reloaded e altri luoghi scritti di Roma*, in *La qualità dell'aria. Storie di questo tempo*, edited by Nicola Lagioia and Christian Raimo, Minimum Fax, Rome, 2004.

Emanuele Trevi, *La 'Roma' di Émile Zola messo all'indice dal Papa*, in *Repubblica-Roma*, March 29, 2007.

Emanuele Trevi, *Il romanzo vero di Walter Siti sulle borgate romane*, in *il manifesto*, April 24, 2008.

Emanuele Trevi, *L'impronta rivelatrice*, in *Alias-La Talpa libri*, May 14, 2011.

Émile Zola, *Mes voyages (Rome)* (1894).

Émile Zola, *Rome* (1895), edited by Jacques Noiray, Gallimard, Paris, 1999.

INDEX

For more information, visit us at www.worldeditions.org.